Working Words in SPELLING

G. Willard Woodruff and George N. Moore
with Robert G. Forest • Donald E. Johnson • Frank DiGiammarino

Illustrated by Will Winslow
Designed by Graphic Associates

D.C. Heath and Company
Lexington, Massachusetts/Toronto, Canada

Be a S-H-A-R-P Speller

See • Look at the word.

Hear • Say the word.

Adopt • Close your eyes.
• Spell the word.

Record • Cover the word.
• Write the word.

Proofread • Check the word.

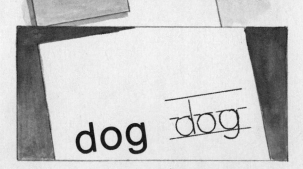

SPELLEX®—a registered trademark of Curriculum Associates, Inc.
SPELLEX® Glossary incorporated by permission of Curriculum Associates, Inc.
Handwriting models in this book are reproduced with permission of Zaner-Bloser, Inc., from the series *HANDWRITING: Basic Skills and Application,* ©1984.
Copyright ©1988 by D.C. Heath and Company
Published simultaneously in Canada
Printed in the United States of America
International Standard Book Number: 0-669-15464-4

13 14 15 16 17 18 19 20

A. Time to Test. Test your words.

B. Words	Shapes	Write
1. bad		_____
2. sad		_____
3. add		_____
4. met		_____
5. wet		_____
6. jet		_____
7. are		_____
8. have		_____

C. Words in Sentences

We had **bad** luck.
The story was **sad**.
Please **add** the numbers.
They **met** us after lunch.

The sand is **wet**.
A **jet** flew above us.
We **are** going to school.
I **have** two cats.

D. Letter Change

Change the underlined letter and write the spelling word.

1. Can you o̲dd four numbers? _____*add*_____

2. A fast l̲et flew in the sky. _____

3. My feet are n̲et. _____

4. I feel very d̲ad. _____

5. We g̲et our friends at the park. _____

6. The h̲ad dog knocked over many plants. _____

7. What time o̲re you leaving? _____

8. They c̲ave a pet monkey. _____

Spelling Words

bad   sad   add   met   wet

jet   are   have

E. Unscramble

Use the letters to write a spelling word for each sentence.

1. aveh   Do you _____*have*_____ a new toy?

2. rea   The cat and the rat _____ fat.

3. dda   Can you _____ these numbers?

4. emt   My father _____ me at the car.

5. twe   I got my shoes _____ at the pond.

6. tje   We flew by _____ .

7. abd   I awoke from a _____ dream.

8. sda   The clown had a _____ face.

F. Missing Vowels

Find the missing vowels and write the spelling words.

1. j _e_ t   ____*jet*____   5. m __ t   _____

2. b __ d   _____   6. w __ t   _____

3. __ dd   _____   7. h __ v __   _____

4. s __ d   _____   8. __ r __   _____

G. ABC Order
Write each pair of spelling words in alphabetical order.

a b c d e f g h i j k l m n o p q r s t u v w x y z

yes, cat _____*cat*_____ , _____*yes*_____

1. jet, have _____ , _____

2. are, bad _____ , _____

3. met, wet _____ , _____

4. sad, add _____ , _____

H. Using Other Word Forms
Circle these words hidden in the word-worm.
Write the words.

adding   badly   has   jets   meet   sadder   were   wettest

az (sadder) caddingpjetsrwettestnwbadlykmeetcwerephasv

1. ____*sadder*____   5. _____

2. _____   6. _____

3. _____   7. _____

4. _____   8. _____

I. I Know My Words. Test your words.

6

Lesson 2

A. Time to Test. Test your words.

B. Words **Shapes** **Write**

1. pin _____

2. win _____

3. hot _____

4. lot _____

5. dot _____

6. bug _____

7. hug _____

8. come _____

C. Words in Sentences

The **pin** is sharp.

We will **win** the game.

The pan is **hot**.

They had a **lot** of fun!

The star looks like a **dot**.

Look at the tiny **bug**.

Grandmother will **hug** us.

Our dog did not **come** home.

D. Letter Change

Change the underlined letter and write the spelling word.

1. The fire was g̲ot. _____

2. Stick it with a t̲in. _____

3. Will you s̲ome with me? _____

4. I like to r̲ug the baby. _____

5. Did you f̲in a prize? _____

6. We have a c̲ot of work to do. _____

7. A little m̲ug flew by. _____

8. Put a n̲ot above the letter i. _____

8

Spelling Words

---

pin   win   hot   lot   dot
bug   hug   come

E. Rhyme Words
Write the spelling words that rhyme.

1. some, _____*come*_____

2. dug, tug, _____ , _____

3. thin, fin, _____ , _____

4. pot, got, _____ , _____ , _____

F. Using Other Word Forms
Add *s* to each spelling word. Write the new word for each sentence.

1. dot + s   Draw _____*dots*_____ on your paper.

2. hug + s   The father _____ his child.

3. pin + s   I need two _____ .

4. come + s   The bus _____ for us each day.

5. bug + s   Some birds eat _____ .

6. win + s   Our team _____ every time.

7. lot + s   I have _____ of friends.

What word was not used? _____

9

G. ABC Order
Write each pair of spelling words in alphabetical order.

a b c d e f g h i j k l m n o p q r s t u v w x y z

1. come, hot _____ , _____

2. win, pin _____ , _____

3. hug, lot _____ , _____

4. dot, bug _____ , _____

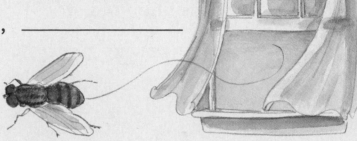

H. Word Change
Write spelling words in place of the underlined words in the sentences. Check your answers in the **Glossary/SPELLEX®**.

1. The <u>fly</u> flew in the window. _____*bug*_____

2. I have a <u>large number</u> of pennies. _____

3. What time will they <u>get here</u>? _____

4. A <u>round spot</u> on the map shows where the

   city is. _____

5. Use a <u>wire with a sharp point</u> to pop the balloon. _____

6. Our horse will <u>be the first to finish</u> the race. _____

7. It is <u>very warm</u> outside. _____

8. Mother will <u>put her arms around</u> me and kiss me. _____

I. I Know My Words. Test your words.

A. Time to Test. Test your words.

B. Words   Shapes   Write

1. tan _____

2. fan _____

3. bet _____

4. set _____

5. leg _____

6. pig _____

7. twig _____

8. were _____

C. Words in Sentences

We used **tan** paint.
The **fan** blows cool air.
They made a **bet**.
Let's **set** the table.

I cut my **leg**.
The **pig** is big.
A **twig** fell from the tree.
We **were** at the park.

D. Unscramble
Use the underlined letters to write the spelling word.

1. We <u>erew</u> the first ones at school. _____

2. I pulled a <u>igtw</u> from the branch. _____

3. What a pretty <u>tse</u> of dishes! _____

4. At the farm we saw a <u>gip</u>. _____

5. The <u>naf</u> will keep us cool. _____

6. I hurt my <u>lge</u> when I fell. _____

7. I <u>teb</u> they are not home. _____

8. My cat is a <u>atn</u> color. _____

E. ABC Order
Write each pair of words in alphabetical order. The words
tan and *twig* have the same first letter. Look at the second letter.

a b c d e f g h i j k l m n o p q r s t u v w x y z

1. set, were _____ , _____

2. bet, fan _____ , _____

3. pig, leg _____ , _____

4. twig, tan _____ , _____

12

Spelling Words

tan	fan	bet	set	leg
pig	twig	were		

F. Using Other Word Forms

Add *s* to each spelling word. Write the new word for each sentence.

1. leg + s   My _____ are long.

2. pig + s   The _____ are eating now.

3. set + s   I have two train _____ .

4. fan + s   The _____ are blowing in both rooms.

5. twig + s   They used _____ to start the fire.

6. tan + s   They have dark _____ .

What two words were not used? _____ _____

G. Missing Vowels

Find the missing vowels and write the spelling words.

1. b __ t _____   5. w __ r __ _____

2. t __ n _____   6. p __ g _____

3. s __ t _____   7. f __ n _____

4. l __ g _____   8. tw __ g _____

H. Word Order

Write a sentence using the words in each group.
Circle the spelling words.

1. here.   the fan   Set

    (Set) the (fan) here. _____

2. I'll bet   is fat.   your pig

    _____

3. tan.   were   The shoes

    _____

4. the twig.   Pick up

    _____

5. I   my leg.   broke

    _____

I. I Know My Words. Test your words.

A. Time to Test. Test your words.

B. Words   **Shapes**   **Write**

1. nap   _____

2. cap   _____

3. men   _____

4. hen   _____

5. fed   _____

6. kid   _____

7. give   _____

8. live   _____

15

C. Words in Sentences

I took a **nap**.

Dad wore a red **cap**.

Those two **men** look alike.

We saw a little **hen**.

I **fed** the dog.

Mother likes to **kid** with me.

Please **give** me the paper.

We **live** in a red house.

D. Unscramble

Use the underlined letters to write a spelling word.

1. The baby is taking a <u>anp</u>. _____

2. The <u>nem</u> ran in a race. _____

3. The rooster and <u>nhe</u> are in the barn. _____

4. My <u>acp</u> is on my head. _____

5. Have you <u>def</u> the cat? _____

6. Did you <u>ivge</u> the dog a cookie? _____

7. A child is sometimes called a <u>dki</u>. _____

8. Where do you <u>ilve</u>? _____

Spelling Words

nap   cap   men   hen   fed

kid   give   live

E. Using Other Word Forms

Add *s* to each spelling word. Write the new word for each sentence.

1. nap + s   My little sister takes _____.

2. live + s   The horse _____ in the barn.

3. kid + s   We laugh when our father _____ us.

4. cap + s   I have two new baseball _____.

5. hen + s   We will feed the _____.

6. give + s   Our teacher _____ us work to do.

What two words were not used?

_____ _____

17

F. Word Change
Write spelling words in place of the underlined words in the sentences. Check your answers in the **Glossary/SPELLEX®**.

1. The baby will <u>sleep for a short time.</u> _____

2. Mother <u>gave food to</u> the fish. _____

3. Are you the only <u>child</u> in your family? _____

4. Please <u>hand over</u> the book to me. _____

5. I will wear my <u>small hat.</u> _____

6. Ants <u>make a home</u> in the ground. _____

7. The <u>chicken</u> laid an egg. _____

8. These <u>boys who have grown up</u> work together. _____

G. Missing Vowels
Find the missing vowels and write the spelling words.

1. h __ n _____

2. k __ d _____

3. f __ d _____

4. n __ p _____

5. l __ v __ _____

6. c __ p _____

7. m __ n _____

8. g __ v __ _____

H. I Know My Words. Test your words.

A. Time to Test. Test your words.

B. Words	**Shapes**	**Write**
1. map		_____
2. clap		_____
3. den		_____
4. pen		_____
5. box		_____
6. fox		_____
7. gone		_____
8. done		_____

19

C. Words in Sentences

This is a world **map**.

We will **clap** our hands.

We watch TV in the **den**.

Do you have a pencil or **pen**?

Put your toys in the **box**.

The **fox** has red fur.

The children have **gone** home.

The work is **done**.

D. Clue Sorting

Use the letters to write a spelling word.

1. d / en   Clue: The fox lives in a ____*den*____ .

2. p   Clue: You write with a _____ .

3. f / ox   Clue: A clever animal is a _____ .

4. b   Clue: You keep things in a _____ .

5. d / one   Clue: If the game is over, it is _____ .

6. g   Clue: If the mitten is lost, it is _____ .

7. m / ap   Clue: To find the way, you use a _____ .

8. cl   Clue: Put your hands together and _____ .

Spelling Words

---

map   clap   den   pen   box

fox   gone   done

E. Using Other Word Forms

Add *s* or *es* to each spelling word.
Write the new word for each sentence.

1. map + s   They used two _____ to find the city.

2. pen + s   I ran out of ink in both _____ .

3. den + s   The lions are sleeping in their _____ .

4. clap + s   The baby laughs and _____ her hands.

5. box + es   We filled the _____ with pictures.

6. fox + es   The _____ are running to their dens.

What two spelling words were not used?

_____ _____

F. Word Order

Write a sentence using the words in each group.
Circle the spelling words.

1. is in the box. The map

   _____

2. in the den. My pen is

   _____

3. until are done. Don't clap they

   _____

4. gone. has The fox

   _____

G. ABC Order

Write each pair of spelling words in alphabetical order.
The words *den* and *done* have the same first letter.
Look at the second letter.

a b c d e f g h i j k l m n o p q r s t u v w x y z

1. fox, map _____ , _____

2. pen, clap _____ , _____

3. gone, box _____ , _____

4. den, done _____ , _____

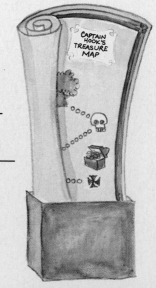

H. I Know My Words. Test your words.

A. Add an s

Add *s* to each spelling word in the sentence.
Write the new word.

1. My family <u>live</u> + s in a red house. _____

2. The baby <u>clap</u> + s his hands when he is happy. _____

3. How many <u>kid</u> + s are there in your family? _____

4. My sister <u>hug</u> + s her friend tightly. _____

5. Our dog <u>nap</u> + s while we are at school. _____

6. Mother <u>bet</u> + s she will be home early. _____

7. Who <u>set</u> + s the table at your house? _____

8. They have a dog with lots of black <u>dot</u> + s. _____

9. My brother <u>add</u> + s numbers on his fingers. _____

10. Our teacher <u>pin</u> + s letters on the board. _____

B. Crossword Puzzle
Use the clues to write these spelling words in the puzzle.

bugs dens jets lots pigs
caps hens legs pens twigs

Across
3. homes for foxes
4. airplanes
7. They have curly tails.
8. used for writing
9. cars in parking _____

Down
1. Ants are _____.
2. birds that lay eggs
5. small sticks
6. small hats
9. Tables have _____.

C. Story Time

Complete the story with these words. Use the number clues.

1	2	3	4	5
had	did	feed	going	won
is	meet	was	gave	came

My pet frog Speedy (1) _____*is*_____ always in frog races.

I went with him to his last race. I (1) _____ never

been before. Speedy brought me to (2) _____ the other

frogs. There were many big frogs. They (2) _____ not

look like they would be very fast. Maybe their owners didn't

(3) _____ them very well. Speedy (3) _____

sure he could win this race. When the race began, Speedy jumped

far and jumped a lot. He was (4) _____ very fast. He

never (4) _____ the other frogs a chance. He

(5) _____ in first! Speedy (5) _____ the

race before the other frogs had even started!

D. Hidden Words

Find these words in the puzzle. The words go across and down. Circle and write each word.

badly   fans   hottest   maps   tans
boxes   foxes   man   saddest   wetter

b	w	e	t	t	e	r	t
a	m	e	f	a	n	s	a
d	a	f	o	x	e	s	n
l	p	o	b	t	d	u	s
y	s	b	o	x	e	s	w
h	o	t	t	e	s	t	m
j	a	x	l	f	n	s	a
s	a	d	d	e	s	t	n

Across

1. _____
2. _____
3. _____
4. _____
5. _____
6. _____

Down

1. _____
2. _____
3. _____
4. _____

A. Time to Test. Test your words.

B. Words	Shapes	Write
1. ten		_____
2. six		_____
3. two		_____
4. four		_____
5. three		_____
6. be		_____
7. baby		_____
8. father		_____
9. here		_____
10. use		_____

C. Words in Sentences

I have **ten** toes.

Are you **six** years old?

I have **two** hands.

The table has **four** legs.

I have **three** sisters.

Please **be** good!

The **baby** is crying.

My **father** has dark hair.

They are **here** now.

You may **use** my pen.

D. Unscramble

Use the underlined letters to write a spelling word.

1. May I <u>seu</u> your crayons? _____

2. I had <u>ent</u> pennies. _____

3. My dog is <u>eethr</u> years old. _____

4. Our street has only <u>ixs</u> houses. _____

5. Try to <u>eb</u> a good speller! _____

6. Will you be <u>ehre</u> on Sunday? _____

7. Is that tall man your <u>aefthr</u>? _____

8. We will be there in <u>wto</u> hours. _____

9. I have <u>rfou</u> new books. _____

10. The <u>byab</u> is learning to walk. _____

28

Spelling Words

ten	six	two	four	three
be	baby	father	here	use

E. Crossword Puzzle

Use the clues to write the spelling words in the puzzle.
Check your answers in the **Glossary/SPELLEX®**.

Across

2. I have _____ legs.
5. after <u>five</u>
6. a young child
7. One, two, _____, go!
9. Come _____ now!
10. Who can it _____?

Down

1. after <u>three</u>
3. May I _____ your skates?
4. not <u>mother</u>
8. one more than <u>nine</u>

29

F. Number Rhymes
Write the number words that complete the rhyme.

One, _t_ _w_ _o_ , buckle my shoe.

___ ___ ___ ___ ___ , ___ ___ ___ ___ , shut the door.

Five, ___ ___ ___ , pick up sticks.

Seven, eight, lay them straight.

Nine, ___ ___ ___ , a big fat hen.

G. Letter Time
Complete the letter with these spelling words.
Use the number clues.

1	2
baby	here be
father	use

Dear Mother,

    Anna and I went to the park with her (1) _____ .

Please do not let the (1) _____ (2) _____ my

toys until I get back (2) _____ . We will

(2) _____ home soon.

             Your son,

             Roberto

H. I Know My Words. Test your words.

A. Time to Test. Test your words.

B. Words	**Shapes**	**Write**
1. rest		_____
2. best		_____
3. nest		_____
4. fast		_____
5. last		_____
6. most		_____
7. lost		_____
8. cook		_____
9. took		_____
10. wood		_____

C. Words in Sentences

It is time to **rest**.

We are **best** friends.

The birds made a **nest**.

I can run **fast**.

What is your **last** name?

I like you the **most**.

They **lost** their ball.

We will **cook** dinner.

Who **took** my pen?

The bat is made of **wood**.

D. Letter Code

Use the letters to write the spelling words.

4 = d
5 = e
6 = f
7 = k
1 = a
2 = b
11 = o
12 = r
13 = s
14 = t
15 = w
8 = l
9 = m
10 = n
3 = c

$\underset{8}{l}\ \underset{11}{o}\ \underset{13}{s}\ \underset{14}{t}$

$\underset{15}{\rule{1em}{0.4pt}}\ \underset{11}{\rule{1em}{0.4pt}}\ \underset{11}{\rule{1em}{0.4pt}}\ \underset{4}{\rule{1em}{0.4pt}}$

$\underset{8}{\rule{1em}{0.4pt}}\ \underset{1}{\rule{1em}{0.4pt}}\ \underset{13}{\rule{1em}{0.4pt}}\ \underset{14}{\rule{1em}{0.4pt}}$

$\underset{10}{\rule{1em}{0.4pt}}\ \underset{5}{\rule{1em}{0.4pt}}\ \underset{13}{\rule{1em}{0.4pt}}\ \underset{14}{\rule{1em}{0.4pt}}$

$\underset{3}{\rule{1em}{0.4pt}}\ \underset{11}{\rule{1em}{0.4pt}}\ \underset{11}{\rule{1em}{0.4pt}}\ \underset{7}{\rule{1em}{0.4pt}}$

$\underset{6}{\rule{1em}{0.4pt}}\ \underset{1}{\rule{1em}{0.4pt}}\ \underset{13}{\rule{1em}{0.4pt}}\ \underset{14}{\rule{1em}{0.4pt}}$

$\underset{9}{\rule{1em}{0.4pt}}\ \underset{11}{\rule{1em}{0.4pt}}\ \underset{13}{\rule{1em}{0.4pt}}\ \underset{14}{\rule{1em}{0.4pt}}$

$\underset{14}{\rule{1em}{0.4pt}}\ \underset{11}{\rule{1em}{0.4pt}}\ \underset{11}{\rule{1em}{0.4pt}}\ \underset{7}{\rule{1em}{0.4pt}}$

$\underset{2}{\rule{1em}{0.4pt}}\ \underset{5}{\rule{1em}{0.4pt}}\ \underset{13}{\rule{1em}{0.4pt}}\ \underset{14}{\rule{1em}{0.4pt}}$

$\underset{12}{\rule{1em}{0.4pt}}\ \underset{5}{\rule{1em}{0.4pt}}\ \underset{13}{\rule{1em}{0.4pt}}\ \underset{14}{\rule{1em}{0.4pt}}$

Now color the parts like this:

4, 6, 8, 10 = red   2, 3, 13 = green   16 = brown

1, 5, 7, 9, 12 = yellow   11, 15 = white   17 = black

14 = blue

32

Spelling Words

rest   best   nest   fast   last
most   lost   cook   took   wood

E. Rhyme Words
Write the spelling words that rhyme.

1. good _____

2. cost _____

3. test _____

_____

_____

4. book _____

_____

5. past _____

_____

6. ghost _____

F. Using Other Word Forms
Add *s*, *ed*, and *ing* to the spelling words.

	+ s	+ ed	+ ing
look	*looks*	*looked*	*looking*
1. last	_____	_____	_____
2. rest	_____	_____	_____
3. cook	_____	_____	_____

33

G. ABC Order

Write each group of spelling words in alphabetical order.
The words *last* and *lost* have the same first letter.
Look at the second letter.

a b c d e f g h i j k l m n o p q r s t u v w x y z

1. cook, best, fast

_____ , _____ , _____

2. nest, rest, most

_____ , _____ , _____

3. wood, took, rest

_____ , _____ , _____

4. most, last, lost

_____ , _____ , _____

H. I Know My Words. Test your words.

Lesson 9

A. Time to Test. Test your words.

B. Words	Shapes	Write
1. doll		_____
2. call		_____
3. hall		_____
4. tall		_____
5. wall		_____
6. walk		_____
7. well		_____
8. duck		_____
9. pull		_____
10. full		_____

C. Words in Sentences

That's a pretty **doll**.
Please **call** me later.
Don't run in the **hall**.
That tree is **tall**.
We will climb over the **wall**.

Do you **walk** to school?
I do not feel **well**.
The **duck** is swimming.
Help me **pull** the wagon.
My cup is **full** of milk.

D. Clues

Use the clues to write the spelling words.

1. to shout _____

2. a toy _____

3. like a fence _____

4. a deep hole for water _____

5. a bird _____

6. a space that joins rooms _____

7. not run _____

8. not push _____

9. not short _____

10. not empty _____

Spelling Words

doll	call	hall	tall	wall
walk	well	duck	pull	full

E. Using Other Word Forms
Add *s*, *ed*, and *ing* to the spelling words.

	+ s	**+ ed**	**+ ing**
1. walk	_____	_____	_____
2. pull	_____	_____	_____
3. call	_____	_____	_____

F. Word Order
Write a sentence using the words in each group.
Circle the spelling words.

1. and the duck | Take | for a walk. | the doll

_____

2. is tall. | in the hall | The wall

_____

3. feel well. | Call me | you | when

_____

4. will pull | full of toys. | the wagon | We

_____

G. ABC Order

Write each group of spelling words in alphabetical order.
Some of the words have the same first letter.
Look at the second letter.

a b c d e f g h i j k l m n o p q r s t u v w x y z

1. walk, pull, full

   _____ , _____ , _____

2. hall, call, doll

   _____ , _____ , _____

3. doll, duck, full

   _____ , _____ , _____

4. well, tall, wall

   _____ , _____ , _____

H. I Know My Words. Test your words.

A. Time to Test. Test your words.

B. Words	**Shapes**	**Write**
1. ate		_____
2. gate		_____
3. late		_____
4. bake		_____
5. came		_____
6. game		_____
7. name		_____
8. same		_____
9. some		_____
10. hope		_____

C. Words in Sentences

We **ate** the pie.

Please close the **gate**.

I was **late** for school.

Let's **bake** bread.

They **came** over to play.

Let's play a **game**.

What is your **name**?

Our shoes are the **same**.

Mother gave us **some** fruit.

I **hope** we have fun.

D. Missing Vowels

Find the missing vowels and write the spelling word.

1. n ___ m ___ _____

2. b ___ k ___ _____

3. h ___ p ___ _____

4. l ___ t ___ _____

5. g ___ m ___ _____

6. c ___ m ___ _____

7. ___ t ___ _____

8. g ___ t ___ _____

9. s ___ m ___ _____

10. s ___ m ___ _____

Spelling Words

ate   gate   late   bake

came   game   name   same

some   hope

E. Letter Scramble

Use the letters to write a spelling word.

1. acem _____
2. emag _____
3. mnae _____
4. esam _____
5. omes _____

6. tae _____
7. tael _____
8. aget _____
9. akeb _____
10. pohe _____

F. Using Other Word Forms

Drop the *e* and add *ed* and *ing* to the spelling words.

	+ ed	+ ing
rake – e	*raked*	*raking*
1. bake – e	_____	_____
2. name – e	_____	_____
3. hope – e	_____	_____

41

G. Letter Time

Complete the letter with the spelling words. Use the number clues.

1	2	3	4	5
name	hope	ate	gate	some
game	came	bake	late	same

Dear Pat,

Let's play a fun (1) _____ ! Can you guess my

(1) _____ ? I (2) _____ you can. Remember

last week when you (2) _____ over to my house?

My mom helped us (3) _____ cookies. When they were

done, we (3) _____ them all up! You did not leave until

(4) _____ . When you left, you forgot to close the

(4) _____ . Next time you come, we can do

(5) _____ of the (5) _____ things.

Well, did you guess who I am?

Guess who!

Your friend,

_____

H. I Know My Words. Test your words.

Lesson 11

A. Time to Test. Test your words.

B. Words	**Shapes**	**Write**
1. **may**		_____
2. **way**		_____
3. **say**		_____
4. **pay**		_____
5. **I'm**		_____
6. **time**		_____
7. **like**		_____
8. **ride**		_____
9. **five**		_____
10. **want**		_____

43

C. Words in Sentences

You **may** go home.
They are on their **way**.
Please **say** that again.
We will **pay** the bill.
Today **I'm** going to the zoo.

It is **time** to eat.
I **like** to play.
We will go for a **ride**.
My cat is **five** years old.
I **want** to go home.

D. Unscramble

Use the underlined letters to write a spelling word.

1. Did you <u>sya</u> yes or no? _____

2. Today <u>mI'</u> going to play football. _____

3. Our house is <u>efvi</u> years old. _____

4. Yes, you <u>yma</u> go to the zoo. _____

5. What do you <u>ntwa</u> for your birthday? _____

6. Do you <u>eidr</u> the bus to school? _____

7. Please <u>apy</u> for the food. _____

8. Most children <u>ikel</u> to play games. _____

9. Which <u>yaw</u> is the lake? _____

10. What <u>temi</u> is it? _____

Spelling Words

may	way	say	pay	I'm
time	like	ride	five	want

E. ABC Order

Write each group of words in alphabetical order.

a b c d e f g h i j k l m n o p q r s t u v w x y z

1. time, may, ride

   _____ , _____ , _____

2. like, five, want

   _____ , _____ , _____

3. pay, way, time

   _____ , _____ , _____

4. say, I'm, like

   _____ , _____ , _____

F. Using Other Word Forms

Add *ed* or *ing* to each spelling word. When a word ends in *e,* drop the *e.* Write the new word for each sentence.

1. say + ing   What are you _____?

2. want + ed   I _____ to go to the park today.

3. pay + ing   Mother is _____ for our ice cream.

4. ride − e + ing   We are _____ our bikes to school.

5. like − e + ed   I _____ the song you sang.

6. time − e + ing   The teacher is _____ us to see how fast we run.

G. Word Order

Write a sentence using the words in each group.
Circle the spelling words.

1. for a ride.   are going   The five of us

_____

2. You   this time.   may pay

_____

3. I'm sorry.   I   to say   want

_____

4. to lead   like   the way.   I

_____

H. I Know My Words. Test your words.

WORKING WITH YOUR WORDS 12

A. More Than One
Add s to the spelling words in each pair.
Write both words.

1. father   Many _____*fathers*_____ like to take their children

    ride   for _____*rides*_____ .

2. nest   We saw two birds' _____ in

    wood   the _____ .

3. wall   The _____ in all the school

    hall   _____ are yellow.

4. duck   Do _____ like to swim in wishing

    well   _____ ?

5. way   There are different _____ to get through

    gate   all the _____ .

6. game   Do you play _____ with

    doll   your _____ ?

B. Fill in the Blanks
Complete each sentence with a spelling word.

five   four   six   ten   three   two

1. The big bad wolf knows the ___ ___ ___ ___ ___ little pigs.

2. I have ___ ___ ___ toes.

3. There are ___ ___ ___ ___ pennies in a nickel.

4. I have ___ ___ ___ eyes.

5. Cats have ___ ___ ___ ___ paws.

6. Ants have ___ ___ ___ legs.

C. Unscramble
Use the letters to write a spelling word for each sentence.

best   here   I'm   may   most   same   some

1. mesa   The three kittens have the _____ color mittens.

2. stbe   Cinderella wore her _____ shoes to the ball.

3. omst   Sleeping Beauty sleeps _____ of the day away.

4. ehre   "Come _____ !" said the scary witch.

5. yma   "You _____ make three wishes," said the Good Fairy.

6. 'mI   Humpty Dumpty fell and said, " _____ a mess."

7. osem   Old Mother Hubbard could not give her dog

_____ bones.

48

D. Making Changes

Add *ed* and *ing* to the spelling words. When a word ends in *e*, drop the *e*.

	+ ed	+ ing
1. rest	_____	_____
2. last	_____	_____
3. cook	_____	_____
4. call	_____	_____
5. pull	_____	_____
6. want	_____	_____
7. walk	_____	_____
8. use – e	_____	_____
9. time – e	_____	_____
10. like – e	_____	_____
11. bake – e	_____	_____
12. name – e	_____	_____
13. hope – e	_____	_____

E. Sentence Fun
Complete the sentences with these words. Use the number clues.

1	2	3	4
take	come	tallest	later
said	babies	lose	been
faster	paid	full	eat

1. "I can run (1) _____ than you can," said the Gingerbread Man.

2. Did Peter Rabbit (1) _____ a carrot from the garden?

3. Little Tommy Tucker (1) _____ he would sing for his supper.

4. How much was (2) _____ for the goose that laid the golden egg?

5. Will Alice (2) _____ to the tea party?

6. The Toymaker makes dolls that look like (2) _____ .

7. How did Cinderella (3) _____ her glass slipper?

8. The giant was the (3) _____ person Jack had ever seen.

9. Jack and Jill spilled a (3) _____ pail of water.

10. The cow will jump over the moon (4) _____ .

11. Peter likes to (4) _____ pumpkins.

12. Little Bo Peep asked, "Where have my sheep

   (4) _____ ?"

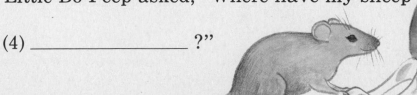

Lesson 13

A. Time to Test. Test your words.

B. Words	**Shapes**	**Write**
1. small		_____
2. bell		_____
3. fell		_____
4. sell		_____
5. hill		_____
6. fill		_____
7. still		_____
8. roll		_____
9. eyes		_____
10. very		_____

C. Words in Sentences

These shoes are too **small**.

Did you hear the **bell**?

The boy **fell** down.

Does that store **sell** bread?

Let's climb the **hill**.

We will **fill** the hole with dirt.

I am **still** hungry.

Please **roll** the ball to me.

My **eyes** are blue.

I am **very** happy.

D. Crossword Puzzle

Use the clues to write the spelling words in the puzzle.
Check your answers in the **Glossary/SPELLEX®**.

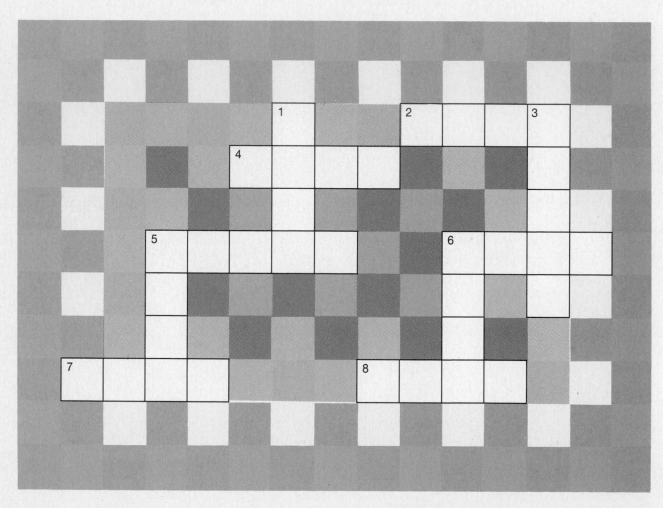

Across

2. ears and _____
4. very, _____ tall
5. not <u>big</u>
6. dropped
7. Roll down the _____ .
8. to turn over and over

Down

1. A _____ rings.
3. not <u>moving</u>
5. not <u>buy</u>
6. one more glass to _____

52

Spelling Words

small	bell	fell	sell	hill
fill	still	roll	eyes	very

E. Using Other Word Forms
Add the endings to the spelling words.
Write the new word for each sentence.

1. hill + s   The _____ are covered with snow.

2. bell + s   We heard the school _____ ringing.

3. fill + ed   My brother _____ the balloon with air.

4. roll + ed   The bead _____ across the floor.

5. sell + ing   Mother is _____ her old car.

F. More Double *L* Words
Use the code to write the spelling words.

f	h	t	m	s	b	r

1. *f* ell   *fell*   5. ▢▢ ill _____

2. ▢▢ all _____   6. ▢ ill _____

3. ▢ ill _____   7. ▢ ell _____

4. ▢ ell _____   8. ▢ oll _____

What two words were not used? _____ _____

G. Word Change

Write the spelling words in place of the underlined words.
Check your answers in the **Glossary/SPELLEX**®.

1. Will the apple <u>keep turning over</u>? _____

2. Everyone has two <u>parts of the face that see</u>. _____

3. Please <u>make full</u> the bowl with soup. _____

4. The <u>high land</u> is covered with grass. _____

5. Did you <u>get money for</u> your old bike? _____

6. A branch <u>dropped</u> to the ground. _____

7. The cow wears a <u>cup that rings</u>. _____

8. Please stand <u>without moving</u>! _____

9. I have <u>little</u> hands. _____

10. I am <u>quite</u> tired. _____

H. I Know My Words. Test your words.

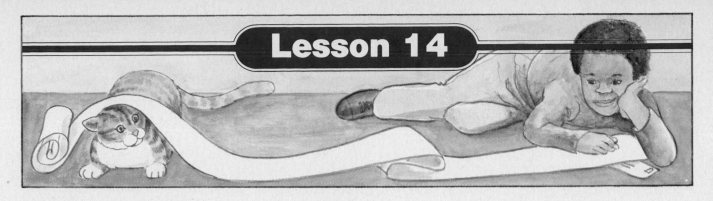

Lesson 14

A. Time to Test. Test your words.

B. Words	Shapes	Write
1. gave		_____
2. cake		_____
3. take		_____
4. end		_____
5. send		_____
6. sent		_____
7. just		_____
8. dust		_____
9. must		_____
10. bus		_____

C. Words in Sentences

Dad **gave** me lunch money.
The **cake** is sweet.
Please **take** us to the zoo.
Where is the **end** of the line?
Did you **send** the gift?

They **sent** me a letter.
Mom **just** got here.
There is **dust** on the chairs.
I **must** be on time.
We missed the **bus**.

D. Rhyme Words
Write the spelling words that rhyme.

1. tent, _____

2. bake, _____ , _____

3. rust, _____ , _____ , _____

4. bend, _____ , _____

5. save, _____

6. us, _____

E. ABC Order
Write the spelling words in alphabetical order.

a b c d e f g h i j k l m n o p q r s t u v w x y z

must, sent, just, gave

_____ , _____ , _____ , _____

Spelling Words

gave   cake   take   end

send   sent   just   dust

must   bus

F. Hidden Words

Find the spelling words hidden in this puzzle.
The words go across and down. Circle and write each word.

Across

1. _____

2. _____

3. _____

4. _____

5. _____

6. _____

Down

1. _____

2. _____

3. _____

4. _____

G. Using Other Word Forms

Add the endings to the spelling words.
Write the new word for each sentence.

1. cake + s   We baked _____ for our school fair.

2. bus + es   School _____ are yellow.

3. end + ed   The show _____ very late.

4. dust + ed   Today I _____ my room.

5. send + ing   I am _____ you a picture of me.

6. take – e + ing Are you _____ us to the movies?

H. Unscramble

Use the underlined letters to write a spelling word.

1. You got here <u>jstu</u> in time! _____

2. We <u>ustm</u> be home by five. _____

3. I like ice cream and <u>ckea</u>. _____

4. Will you <u>atek</u> me to the zoo? _____

5. Will you <u>esnd</u> me your picture? _____

6. I <u>ntes</u> my grandmother flowers. _____

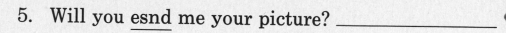

7. We live at the <u>nde</u> of this street. _____

8. Our class rode on the school <u>sbu</u>. _____

9. My old toy was covered with <u>udst</u>. _____

10. My friend <u>evga</u> me a book to read. _____

I. I Know My Words. Test your words.

A. Time to Test. Test your words.

B. Words	Shapes	Write
1. rang		_____
2. hang		_____
3. ring		_____
4. sing		_____
5. long		_____
6. song		_____
7. better		_____
8. letter		_____
9. butter		_____
10. water		_____

C. Words in Sentences

Who **rang** the bell?
Let's **hang** the picture.
What a pretty gold **ring**!
We will **sing** together.
My hair is **long**.

It is a happy **song**.
I feel much **better**.
I wrote you a **letter**.
We ate bread with **butter**.
This **water** is warm.

D. Crossword Puzzle

Use the clues to write the spelling words in the puzzle.
Check your answers in the **Glossary/SPELLEX**®.

Across

4. bread and _____
5. Did the telephone _____ ?
7. Sing a _____ .
8. It's wet.
9. The bell _____ .

Down

1. a picture to _____
2. to write a _____
3. a song to _____
4. doing much _____ in math
6. not short, but _____

Spelling Words

rang   hang   ring   sing
long   song   better   letter
butter   water

E. Word Balloons

Write the spelling words that end with *ng*.
Write the spelling words that end with *ter*.

ng

_____ _____

_____ _____

_____ _____

ter

_____

_____

_____

F. Using Other Word Forms
Add *s* and *ing* to the spelling words.

	+ s	**+ ing**
1. ring	_____	_____
2. sing	_____	_____
3. hang	_____	_____

G. Word Order
Write a sentence using the words in each group.
Circle the spelling words.

1. sing the song.   as you   Ring the bell

_____

2. a long letter.   me   Write

_____

3. you rang   Hang the bell   here.

_____

4. will feel better.   and you   some water   Drink

_____

5. Spread   on your toast.   some butter

_____

H. I Know My Words. Test your words.

Lesson 16

A. Time to Test. Test your words.

B. Words   **Shapes**   **Write**

1. car _____

2. card _____

3. cart _____

4. far _____

5. farm _____

6. tar _____

7. barn _____

8. bark _____

9. dark _____

10. park _____

C. Words in Sentences

We bought a new **car**.
They sent us a **card**.
The ox pulls a **cart**.
They live **far** away.
Animals live on a **farm**.

The **tar** is hot!
Our cow is in the **barn**.
My dog has a loud **bark**.
Is it **dark** outside?
We play at the **park**.

D. Unscramble

Use the underlined letters to write a spelling word.

1. The workers laid new <u>atr</u> on our street. _____

2. We jumped into the hay in the <u>abrn</u>. _____

3. My aunt sent me a get-well <u>rdca</u>. _____

4. We drove around in the new <u>rac</u>. _____

5. My sister is afraid of the <u>adrk</u>. _____

6. Our camp was <u>raf</u> from stores. _____

7. Where did you <u>rkpa</u> the car? _____

8. Some trees have white <u>rkba</u>. _____

9. I liked our visit to the <u>frma</u>. _____

10. The <u>rtca</u> has two wheels. _____

E. ABC Order

Write the spelling words in alphabetical order.

tar, far, dark

_____ , _____ , _____

Spelling Words

car	card	cart	far	farm
tar	barn	bark	dark	park

F. Clues

Use the clues to write the spelling words.

1. a machine with four wheels _____

2. It's black and covers roads. _____

3. a building on a farm _____

4. where food is grown _____

5. sent on birthdays _____

6. a place to play _____

7. Dogs do this. _____

8. not bright _____

9. a wagon _____

10. not near _____

G. Using Other Word Forms
Use these words to complete the sentences.

barking   cards   carts   parking   barns   cars   farming

1. We can park two _____ in our garage.

2. My friends sent me birthday _____ .

3. Horses are used to pull _____ .

4. The farmer is _____ the field.

5. Cows sleep inside _____ .

6. Mother is _____ the car.

7. Why is the dog _____ ?

H. Rhyme Words
Write the spelling words that rhyme.

1. arm, _____   4. hard, _____

2. yarn, _____   5. part, _____

3. jar, _____ ,   6. mark, _____ ,

_____ ,   _____ ,

_____   _____

I. I Know My Words. Test your words.

A. Time to Test. Test your words.

B. Words   **Shapes**   **Write**

1. arm   _____

2. star   _____

3. hard   _____

4. bird   _____

5. work   _____

6. bite   _____

7. side   _____

8. fine   _____

9. nine   _____

10. fire   _____

C. Words in Sentences

My **arm** is caught in my coat.
I saw a shining **star**.
This bed is too **hard**.
The **bird** flew away.
Where do you **work**?

Our dog won't **bite** you.
Read this **side** of the page.
Today was a **fine** day.
Our dog had **nine** puppies.
The **fire** is hot!

D. Unscramble

Use the underlined letters to write the spelling word.

1. Wash the apple before you <u>iebt</u> into it. _____

2. We need more wood for the <u>iref</u>. _____

3. He uses his left <u>rma</u> to pitch. _____

4. Name a <u>irdb</u> that cannot fly. _____

5. I made a wish upon a <u>rast</u>. _____

6. She slept on her left <u>dsie</u>. _____

7. My father is a <u>fnei</u> cook. _____

8. After eight comes <u>inen</u>. _____

9. Let's <u>orkw</u> on a puzzle. _____

10. A rock is <u>ahrd</u>. _____

68

Spelling Words

| arm | star | hard | bird | work |
| bite | side | fine | nine | fire |

E. Guide Words
The word pairs below are guide words from the **Glossary/SPELLEX®**. Write the words from the spelling list that appear on the same page as the guide words.

add—bake

arm

bet—box

_____

_____

fast—flower

_____

_____

hang—hot

_____

never—park

_____

shut—sold

_____

some—stick

_____

winter—zoo

_____

F. Using Other Word Forms

Use the clues to write the words in the blanks.
Then use the boxed letters to write a hidden word.

arms   bites   stars   birds   sides   worked

1. a mother bird and six baby _____   b i r d s

2. A square has four _____ .   __ □ __ __ __

3. up in the night sky   __ □ __ __ __

4. not played   __ __ __ __ □ __

5. have hands on the ends   __ __ __ □

HIDDEN WORD: cuts into with teeth   __ __ __ __ __

G. Rhyme Words

Write the spelling words that rhyme.

line, _____ , _____

tire, _____

card, _____

H. I Know My Words. Test your words.

A. Add *s* or *es*

Add *s* or *es* to each spelling word in the sentence.
Write the new word.

1. My friends sent me card + s when I was sick. _____

2. My mother sends letter + s to her friend. _____

3. Hens, ducks, and geese arc all bird + s. _____

4. Our cat has bell + s around its neck. _____

5. Do you know how to bake cake + s? _____

6. I like to ride my bike over hill + s. _____

7. Paint the side + s of the box blue. _____

8. I will help Dad wash both car + s. _____

9. We rode on three bus + es today. _____

10. I hurt my arm + s when I fell. _____

11. We counted four red barn + s. _____

12. The sun is one of the star + s. _____

13. Fill the cart + s with corn. _____

B. Making Changes

Add *ed* and *ing* to the spelling words.
Change *fire* and *tar* when *ed* and *ing* are added.

	+ ed	+ ing
1. fill	_____	_____
2. park	_____	_____
3. work	_____	_____
4. farm	_____	_____
5. dust	_____	_____
6. end	_____	_____
7. bark	_____	_____
8. butter	_____	_____
9. roll	_____	_____
10. water	_____	_____
11. fire – e	_____	_____
12. tar + r	_____	_____

C. Hidden Words

Find these words in the puzzle. The words go across and down.
Circle and write each word.

bit	hanging	sang	sends
falls	ringing	selling	songs
giving	rings	sending	took

h	r	i	n	g	s	t	k	o	g
a	b	t	r	i	n	g	i	n	g
n	s	a	b	c	x	s	p	w	l
g	a	g	i	v	i	n	g	t	s
i	n	v	e	b	n	f	p	o	e
n	g	h	k	i	r	a	s	o	l
g	e	n	s	t	k	l	o	k	l
p	s	e	n	d	s	l	n	y	i
m	h	n	g	n	g	s	g	s	n
s	e	n	d	i	n	g	s	e	g

Across

1. _____
2. _____
3. _____
4. _____
5. _____

Down

1. _____
2. _____
3. _____
4. _____
5. _____
6. _____
7. _____

D. *Er* and *Est*

Add *er* and *est* to the spelling words.
Drop the final *e* before adding *er* or *est* to the word *fine*.

		+ er	+ est
1.	dark	*darker*	*darkest*
2.	hard	_____	_____
3.	long	_____	_____
4.	small	_____	_____
5.	fine – e	_____	_____

E. Sentence Fun

Complete the sentences with these spelling words.
Use the number clues.

1	2	3	4
better	far	must	very
eyes	just	nine	still

1. Red Riding Hood lives (2) _____ from
   Grandmother's house.

2. "What big (1) _____ you have!" cried Red Riding Hood.

3. "The (1) _____ to see you with," said the wolf.

4. Cinderella (3) _____ leave the ball
   by twelve o'clock!

5. The Cat in the Hat has (3) _____ lives.

6. Snow White has (4) _____ white skin.

7. Is Sleeping Beauty (4) _____ asleep?

8. The king's men (2) _____ could not
   put Humpty Dumpty together again.

A. Time to Test. Test your words.

B. Words	**Shapes**	**Write**
1. low		_____
2. blow		_____
3. slow		_____
4. show		_____
5. how		_____
6. town		_____
7. down		_____
8. flower		_____
9. ago		_____
10. goes		_____

C. Words in Sentences

The bridge is **low**.
The wind will **blow**.
Turtles are **slow**.
Please **show** us the way.
We will learn **how**.

We live in a small **town**.
They ran **down** the hill.
I will pick a **flower**.
It happened a long time **ago**.
Mother **goes** to work early.

D. Boat Riddles

Use the clues to write the *ow* spelling words.

1. not <u>high</u> _____

2. not <u>fast</u> _____

3. to push out air _____

4. not a <u>city</u> _____

5. A rose is one. _____

6. a TV program _____

7. Show me _____ . _____

8. not <u>up</u> _____

E. Crossword Puzzle

Use the clues to write two spelling words in the puzzle.

1. in the past

2. moves →

76

Spelling Words

low	blow	slow	show
how	town	down	flower
ago	goes		

F. Using Other Word Forms

Add *s* and *ing* to the *ow* spelling words.

	+ s	+ ing
1. blow	_____	_____
2. slow	_____	_____
3. show	_____	_____
4. flower	_____	_____

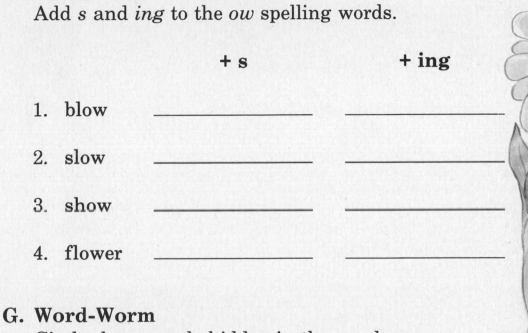

G. Word-Worm

Circle these words hidden in the word-worm.
Write the words.

ago down goes how low town

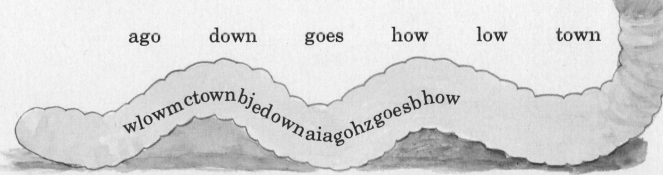

wlowmctownbjedownaiagohzgoesbhow

1. _____ 3. _____ 5. _____

2. _____ 4. _____ 6. _____

H. Letter Change
Change the letters to write the spelling words.

blow   1. Change the <u>b</u> to <u>s</u> and get

"Please go _____ !"

bow   2. Change the <u>b</u> to <u>l</u> and get

"The tide is _____ ."

slow   3. Change the <u>l</u> to <u>h</u> and get

"to point out." _____

gown   4. Change the <u>g</u> to <u>t</u> and get

"smaller than a city." _____

low   5. Add a <u>b</u> before the <u>l</u> and get

"Let's _____ out the candles."

show   6. Drop the <u>s</u> and get

"I know _____ to play the piano."

flow   7. Add <u>er</u> and get

"a pretty plant." _____

town   8. Change the <u>t</u> to <u>d</u> and get "Sit _____ ."

does   9. Change the <u>d</u> to <u>g</u> and get

"moves from one place to another." _____

go   10. Add <u>a</u> before <u>g</u> and get "before now." _____

I. I Know My Words. Test your words.

Lesson 20

A. Time to Test. Test your words.

B. Words	**Shapes**	**Write**
1. house		_____
2. found		_____
3. round		_____
4. clock		_____
5. block		_____
6. sick		_____
7. pick		_____
8. stick		_____
9. word		_____
10. corn		_____

C. Words in Sentences

We live in a brick **house**.
I **found** my mitten!
A ball is **round**.
The **clock** is ticking.
Where is the toy **block**?

I feel **sick**.
Which book did you **pick**?
Pick up that **stick**.
Can you spell this **word**?
We ate fresh **corn**.

D. Crossword Puzzle

Use the clues to write the spelling words in the puzzle.
Check your answers in the **Glossary/SPELLEX**®.

Across

4. a home
7. It keeps time.
8. a crop of _____
9. I will _____ a flower.
10. a two-letter _____

Down

1. a toy with six sides
2. a thin piece of wood
3. looked for and _____
5. not well
6. the shape of a ball

Spelling Words

house	found	round	clock
block	sick	pick	stick
word	corn		

E. Using Other Word Forms

Use the clues to write the words in the blanks.
Then use the boxed letters to write a hidden word.

blocks   houses   picks   words
clocks   picking   sticks

1. Paste does this.   __ __ __ ☐ __ __ __

2. Children play with them.   __ ☐ __ __ __ __

3. Sentences have them.   __ ☐ __ __ __

4. chooses   __ __ ☐ __ __

5. choosing   __ __ __ ☐ __ __ __

6. one house, two ____   __ __ ☐ __ __ __

HIDDEN WORD: They tell us what time it is.

__ __ __ __ __ __

81

F. Rhyme Words
Write the spelling words that rhyme.

1. kick, _____

_____

2. horn, _____

3. ground, _____

_____

G. Letter Code
Use the code to write the spelling words.

1 = b
4 = e
7 = i
10 = n
2 = c
8 = k
11 = o
5 = f
9 = l
3 = d
6 = h
12 = p

13 = r
14 = s
15 = t
16 = u
17 = w

1. ___ ___ ___ ___
   2 11 13 10

2. ___ ___ ___ ___ ___
   6 11 16 14 4

3. ___ ___ ___ ___ ___
   14 15 7 2 8

4. ___ ___ ___ ___
   17 11 13 3

5. ___ ___ ___ ___ ___
   1 9 11 2 8

6. ___ ___ ___ ___ ___
   2 9 11 2 8

7. ___ ___ ___ ___
   14 7 2 8

8. ___ ___ ___ ___ ___
   13 11 16 10 3

9. ___ ___ ___ ___ ___
   5 11 16 10 3

10. ___ ___ ___ ___
    12 7 2 8

H. I Know My Words. Test your words.

A. Time to Test. Test your words.

B. Words	Shapes	Write
1. candy		_____
2. sandy		_____
3. today		_____
4. tonight		_____
5. dish		_____
6. fish		_____
7. miss		_____
8. sister		_____
9. winter		_____
10. other		_____
11. brother		_____
12. beside		_____

C. Words in Sentences

The **candy** is soft.
Beaches are **sandy**.
My birthday is **today**.
We are leaving **tonight**.
My **dish** is clean.
I caught a **fish**!

I will **miss** you.
This is my big **sister**.
It was a cold **winter**.
They were here the **other** day.
My baby **brother** sat up.
I sat **beside** my friend.

D. Letter Scramble

Use the letters to write spelling words.

1. terniw _____

2. ntoight _____

3. tersis _____

4. thoer _____

5. thbroer _____

6. shdi _____

7. ssmi _____

8. dsiebe _____

9. dyato _____

10. dycna _____

11. ansdy _____

12. shfi _____

84

Spelling Words

candy   sandy   today   tonight
dish   fish   miss   sister
winter   other   brother   beside

E. Word Change

Write a spelling word in place of the underlined words in each sentence. Check your answers in the **Glossary/SPELLEX®**.

1. May I sit <u>next to</u> you? _____

2. I will see you <u>on this night.</u> _____

3. They will <u>not reach</u> the bus. _____

4. Our road is <u>covered with sand.</u> _____

5. Put the fruit in a <u>plate or bowl.</u> _____

6. I am going skating <u>on this day.</u> _____

7. That girl is my <u>parents' daughter.</u> _____

8. I like <u>the coldest season of the year.</u> _____

9. My <u>parents' son</u> has gone to school. _____

10. We ate a <u>sweet food made from sugar.</u> _____

11. Please take this one or the <u>one that is left.</u> _____

12. The <u>animal that lives in water</u> ate the worm. _____

F. Using Other Word Forms

Add *s* or *es* to each spelling word. Write the new word for each sentence.

1. sister + s   My _____ are older than I am.

2. dish + es   Please put the _____ away.

3. winter + s   Most _____ are long and cold.

4. miss + es   Grandmother _____ us.

5. brother + s   Both your _____ are very tall.

6. fish + es   My brother _____ with worms.

G. Guide Words

The word pairs below are guide words from the **Glossary/SPELLEX®**. Write the words from the spelling list that appear on the same page as the guide words.

band—best
_____

fast—flower
_____

shut—sold
_____

bread—came
_____

men—nest
_____

think—trip
_____

camp—cold
_____

never—park
_____

_____

winter—zoo
_____

dip—each
_____

same—show
_____

H. I Know My Words. Test your words.

A. Time to Test. Test your words.

B. Words	Shapes	Write
1. or		_____
2. more		_____
3. store		_____
4. horse		_____
5. forget		_____
6. forgot		_____
7. even		_____
8. ever		_____
9. never		_____
10. every		_____
11. dear		_____
12. year		_____

C. Words in Sentences

Was the news good **or** bad?

Do you want **more**?

The shoe **store** closes early.

The **horse** likes carrots.

Don't **forget** to call.

I **forgot** my lunch.

Is the number odd or **even**?

We won't **ever** know.

They are **never** on time.

We run **every** day.

This is my **dear** friend.

I will be eight next **year**.

D. Crossword Puzzle

Use the clues to write the spelling words in the puzzle.
Check your answers in the **Glossary/SPELLEX**®.

Across

1. place to buy things
3. not <u>less</u>
6. not to remember
8. The game score is _____ .
9. twelve months
11. not a <u>pony</u>

Down

2. all or each one
4. Are you hot _____ cold?
5. Have you _____ seen a bear?
6. did not remember
7. not <u>ever</u>
10. much loved

Spelling Words

or	more	store	horse
forget	forgot	even	ever
never	every	dear	year

E. Using Other Word Forms

Use the clues to write the words in the blanks.
Then use the boxed letters to write a hidden word.

dearest   forgetting   most   years
forgets   horses   stores

1. almost all   __ __ □ __

2. not <u>remembering</u>   __ __ __ __ □ __ __ __ __ __

3. large animals with four legs   __ __ __ □ __ __ __

4. one year, two ____   __ __ __ □ __

5. never remembers   __ __ __ __ □ __ __ __

6. the most loved   __ __ __ __ □ __ __

HIDDEN WORD: places to buy things   __ __ __ __ __ __

89

F. Letter Time

Complete the letter with the spelling words. Use the number clues.

1	2	3	4
forget	year	even	or
ever	every	store	dear
forgot	never	horse	more

Dear Fran,

I bet you thought I (1) _____ your birthday. How

could I (1) _____ (1) _____ ? I would

(2) _____ let it go by. You remember my birthday

(2) _____ (2) _____ . Yesterday I rode my

(3) _____ to the (3) _____ to buy you a

card. I counted an (3) _____ number of pennies. I

found out that I needed a dime, (4) _____ ten

(4) _____ pennies. So, this letter is your birthday card

instead. Happy Birthday!

Your (4) _____ friend,

Lee

G. I Know My Words. Test your words.

A. Time to Test. Test your words.

B. Words	Shapes	Write

1. gas _____

2. apple _____

3. rabbit _____

4. bunny _____

5. funny _____

6. summer _____

7. supper _____

8. dinner _____

9. dress _____

10. looked _____

11. looking _____

12. door _____

C. Words in Sentences

The car needs **gas**.

This **apple** is sour!

We saw a hopping **rabbit**.

Our pet **bunny** is soft.

The clown was **funny**.

It was a hot **summer**.

Soon we will eat **supper**.

Is **dinner** ready?

I like to **dress** up.

They **looked** for the key.

Father is **looking** for us.

Please open the **door**.

D. Double Fun

Find the missing double letters. Then write the spelling words.

pp   mm   bb   nn   oo   ss

1. ra _b_ _b_ it   _rabbit_

2. a ___ ___ le   _____

3. fu ___ ___ y   _____

4. l ___ ___ ked   _____

5. dre ___ ___   _____

6. d ___ ___ r   _____

7. di ___ ___ er   _____

8. su ___ ___ er   _____

9. su ___ ___ er   _____

10. bu ___ ___ y   _____

11. l ___ ___ king   _____

What spelling word does not have double letters?

_____

Spelling Words

gas	apple	rabbit	bunny
funny	summer	supper	dinner
dress	looked	looking	door

E. Using Other Word Forms

Add *s* or *es* to the spelling words. For words that end in *y*, change the *y* to *i* and add *es*.

+ s

ladder _____*ladders*_____

1. rabbit _____
2. apple _____
3. summer _____
4. dinner _____
5. supper _____
6. door _____

+ es

class _____*classes*_____

7. dress _____
8. gas _____

y to i + es

penny _____*pennies*_____

9. funny _____
10. bunny _____

F. Letter Scramble

Use the letters to write the spelling words.

1. uybnn

_____

2. rood

_____

3. bbtira

_____

4. koolde

_____

5. epprsu

_____

6. suermm

_____

7. alepp

_____

8. ssedr

_____

9. sag

_____

10. dirnne

_____

11. ooklngi

_____

12. nnfuy

_____

G. Guide Words

The word pairs below are guide words from the **Glossary/SPELLEX**®. Write the words from the spelling list that appear on the same page as the guide words.

add—bake

_____

bread—came

_____

come—dinner

_____

dip—each

_____

_____

funny—hall

_____

_____

looked—meet

_____

_____

part—rabbit

_____

still—thin

_____

_____

H. I Know My Words. Test your words.

A. Word Math

Follow the signs to write new words. For words that end in *y*, change the *y* to *i* before adding *es*.

1. block + ing = _____

2. dinner + s = _____

3. fish + ed = _____

4. gas + es = _____

5. town + s = _____

6. word + s = _____

7. dish + es = _____

8. clock + s = _____

9. supper + s = _____

10. dress + es = _____

11. summer + s = _____

12. bunny – y + ies = _____

13. candy – y + ies = _____

14. funny – y + ies = _____

B. Story Time
Complete the story with these words. Use the number clues.

1	2	3	4	5
looked	blowing	flowers	gone	missed
find	stores	picked	evenly	look
sticks	forgetting	showed	forgot	

I love the way peanut butter (1) _____ to the roof of

my mouth. This afternoon I (1) _____ for a jar on the

shelf. Of course, I couldn't (1) _____ any. We're

always (2) _____ to replace the jar. Food

(2) _____ should have signs that say, "You need

peanut butter!"

On my way to the store, I watched some kites that were

(2) _____ in the wind. One child (3) _____

me how to make a kite fly high. Then I saw some pretty

(3) _____ . I (3) _____ a few and placed

them (4) _____ in my hand.

By the time I got to the store, it was late. I (4) _____

what I had come to buy. When I got home, my mother said that I

had been (4) _____ a long time. She was just about to

(5) _____ for me. I had (5) _____ supper.

Even worse, I still had no peanut butter!

C. Sentence Fun
Complete the sentences with these spelling words.
Use the number clues.

1	2	3	4	5
down	corn	how	ever	every
winter	beside	tonight	other	or
ago	never	more	today	sandy

1. Sleeping Beauty fell asleep many years (1) _____ .

2. Jack fell (1) _____ and broke his crown.

3. Frosty the Snowman can be seen in the (1) _____ .

4. A spider sat down (2) _____ Little Miss Muffet.

5. Humpty Dumpty will (2) _____ sit on a wall again.

6. Did Old MacDonald grow (2) _____ on his farm?

7. Do you know (3) _____ many little pigs there were?

8. Baa-Baa Black Sheep had (3) _____ bags of wool.

9. The cow will jump over the moon (3) _____ .

10. Cinderella's shoes fit no (4) _____ person.

11. Have you (4) _____ seen a hen lay a golden egg?

12. The sky fell on Chicken Little (4) _____ .

13. Did the mouse run up (5) _____ down the clock?

14. Snow White liked (5) _____ dwarf she met.

15. The Ugly Duckling's feet

    were (5) _____ .

D. *Er* and *Est*

Add *er* or *est* to each spelling word.
Write the new word for each sentence.

1. slow + est   Is the turtle the _____ animal?

2. dear + est   Come meet my _____ friends.

3. low + er   The water is _____ at one end
of the pool.

4. sick + er   I felt _____ yesterday than
I do today.

5. round + est   That's the _____ pumpkin I've
ever seen.

SLOWEST ANIMAL CONTEST

E. More Than One

Add *s* to the spelling words in each pair.
Write both words.

1. brother
sister   How many _____ and _____
do you have?

2. rabbit
apple   Do _____ like to eat _____ ?

3. house
door   Most _____ have _____ .

4. horse
year   I rode _____ for many _____ .

Lesson 25

A. Time to Test. Test your words.

B. Words	**Shapes**	**Write**
1. too		_____
2. cool		_____
3. room		_____
4. noon		_____
5. soon		_____
6. food		_____
7. need		_____
8. feed		_____
9. feet		_____
10. week		_____
11. green		_____
12. sleep		_____

C. Words in Sentences

This soup is **too** hot!
It is **cool** outside.
Clean your **room**.
The bell rings at **noon**.
They will be here **soon**.
I ate too much **food**!

They **need** more time.
Who will **feed** the dog?
My **feet** are sore.
They visit once a **week**.
The grass is so **green**.
Now it is time to **sleep**.

D. Letter Twins

Use the clues to write the *oo* and *ee* spelling words.

oo

1. _____*room*_____
   clue: in a house

2. _____
   clue: something to eat

3. _____
   clue: not <u>warm</u>

4. _____
   clue: in a short time

5. _____
   clue: 12 o'clock

6. _____
   clue: also

ee

1. _____
   clue: a color

2. _____
   clue: seven days

3. _____
   clue: give food to

4. _____
   clue: rest in bed

5. _____
   clue: must have

6. _____
   clue: more than one foot

Spelling Words

too	cool	room	noon
soon	food	need	feed
feet	week	green	sleep

E. Using Other Word Forms

Circle the words hidden in the word-worm.
Write the words.

cooled	greener	foot	slept	weeks
fed	needed	rooms	sooner	

stroomsineededoafedthweeksrosleptcooledsoonerkfootsgreenerj

1. _____   4. _____   7. _____

2. _____   5. _____   8. _____

3. _____   6. _____   9. _____

F. Rhyme Words

Write the spelling words that rhyme.

moon, _____

_____

mood, _____

new, _____

G. Think Time

Write a sentence that uses the two spelling words.

1. wood, hard   *This wood is very hard.* _____

   _____

2. too, cool _____

   _____

3. sleep, feed _____

   _____

4. food, week _____

   _____

5. room, green _____

   _____

6. noon, soon _____

   _____

7. feet, need _____

   _____

H. I Know My Words. Test your words.

A. Time to Test. Test your words.

B. Words	**Shapes**	**Write**
1. lamp		_____
2. camp		_____
3. band		_____
4. bath		_____
5. both		_____
6. lunch		_____
7. beach		_____
8. dip		_____
9. hit		_____
10. city		_____
11. wish		_____
12. find		_____

C. Words in Sentences

Is the **lamp** on?

We are going to **camp** out.

The **band** was loud.

I took a **bath**.

Carry it with **both** hands.

We ate **lunch** outside.

They swam at the **beach**.

I will **dip** the brush in the paint.

I will **hit** the ball.

We live in the **city**.

Make a **wish**!

Did you **find** the button?

D. Crossword Puzzle

Use the clues to write the spelling words in the puzzle.
Check your answers in the **Glossary/SPELLEX**®.

Across

3. music makers
5. not <u>lose</u>
7. a place for tents
8. ocean shore
10. It means "two."
11. to slap

Down

1. the noon meal
2. a light
4. to hope for
6. to put in and pull out
8. to take a hot _____
9. a big town

Spelling Words

---

lamp	camp	band	bath
both	lunch	beach	dip
hit	city	wish	find

E. Letter Change

Change the underlined letter and write a spelling word.

1. I s̲it a home run! _____

2. I d̲ish I had a pet rabbit. _____

3. We had fun at the r̲each. _____

4. We found d̲oth of his shoes. _____

5. Did you w̲ind your lost cap? _____

6. I spent two weeks at a d̲amp. _____

7. It's time to turn the cam̲p on. _____

8. The s̲and played at our party. _____

9. What did you bring for b̲unch? _____

10. My aunt loves to visit the m̲ity. _____

11. I like to s̲ip my toes in the lake. _____

12. Warm water is best for your m̲ath. _____

F. Unscramble
Use the letters to write the spelling words.

1. t i h
2. i f n d
3. p d i
4. n d b a
5. t i c y
6. l a m p
7. s h h w i
8. m p a c
9. t h a b
10. o b t h
11. c h e a b
12. c h u n l

1. _____hit_____   5. _____   9. _____

2. _____   6. _____   10. _____

3. _____   7. _____   11. _____

4. _____   8. _____   12. _____

G. Using Other Word Forms
Add *s* or *es* to the spelling words.
For the word that ends in *y*, change the *y* to *i* and add *es*.

+ s   **+ es**

1. lamp _____   7. lunch _____

2. band _____   8. wish _____

3. hit _____   9. beach _____

4. camp _____   **y to i + es**

5. dip _____   10. city _____

6. find _____

H. I Know My Words. Test your words.

106

A. Time to Test. Test your words.

B. Words	**Shapes**	**Write**
1. zoo		_____
2. boots		_____
3. log		_____
4. open		_____
5. home		_____
6. know		_____
7. jumped		_____
8. by		_____
9. die		_____
10. been		_____
11. son		_____
12. from		_____

C. Words in Sentences

We saw lions at the **zoo**.
Put your **boots** on.
They own a **log** cabin.
The window is **open**.
Welcome to our **home**.
Do you **know** them?

The dog **jumped** up.
Sit **by** the tree.
Will the flowers **die**?
We have **been** away.
This is our **son**.
Apples fell **from** the tree.

D. Unscramble

Use the underlined letters to write the spelling word.

1. Stand <u>yb</u> my side. _____

2. Where have you <u>nebe</u>? _____

3. Do you <u>wkno</u> his name? _____

4. We <u>dmpuej</u> over the rope. _____

5. We went <u>mfro</u> here to there. _____

6. Did you leave the door <u>eonp</u>? _____

7. She walked <u>mheo</u> from school. _____

8. The <u>lgo</u> burned in the fireplace. _____

9. They have a daughter and a <u>osn</u>. _____

10. My <u>obtso</u> don't fit my feet anymore. _____

11. If you do not water a plant, it will <u>ied</u>. _____

12. Many different animals live at the <u>ozo</u>. _____

Spelling Words

zoo	boots	log	open
home	know	jumped	by
die	been	son	from

E. Using Other Word Forms

Use the clues to write the words in the blanks.
Then use the boxed letters to write a hidden word.

died	jumping	logs	sons
homes	knew	opening	zoos

1. places to see wild animals ___ ☐ ___ ___

2. leaping ___ ___ ___ ☐ ___ ___ ___

3. houses ___ ___ ___ ☐ ___

4. not daughters ___ ___ ☐ ___

5. stopped living ___ ___ ☐ ___

6. was sure of ___ ___ ☐ ___

7. pieces of wood ___ ☐ ___ ___

HIDDEN WORD: not closing

___ ___ ___ ___ ___ ___ ___

F. ABC Order

Write the words in alphabetical order.
The words *by, boots,* and *been* have the same first letter.
Look at the second letter.

a b c d e f g h i j k l m n o p q r s t u v w x y z

from, by, boots, been

_____ , _____ , _____ , _____

G. Think Time

Write a sentence that uses the two spelling words.

1. know, son _____

_____

2. open, zoo _____

_____

3. jumped, boots _____

_____

4. die, from _____

_____

5. log, by _____

_____

6. home, been _____

_____

H. I Know My Words. Test your words.

Lesson 28

A. Time to Test. Test your words.

B. Words   **Shapes**   **Write**

1. try

2. cry

3. dry

4. fry

5. sky

6. fly

7. tree

8. think

9. what

10. who

11. why

12. where

C. Words in Sentences

You must **try** again.
Did the baby **cry**?
My hair is **dry**.
Can you **fry** an egg?
The **sky** is blue.
Birds **fly** high.

Let's climb a **tree**.
Please **think** quickly!
I don't know **what** to do.
We know **who** they are.
I don't know **why** you're mad.
I wonder **where** it is!

D. Letter Code

Use the code to write the spelling words.

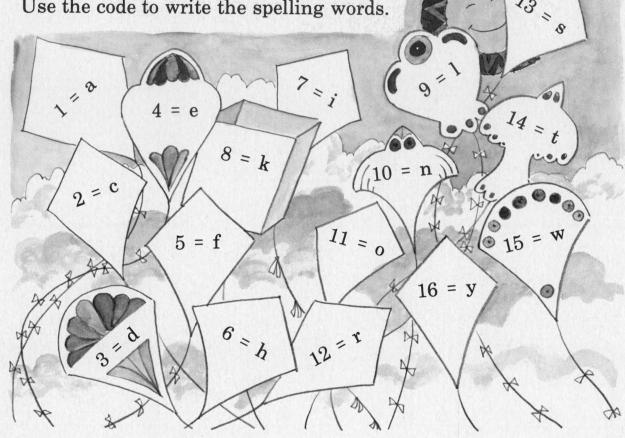

1 = a
2 = c
3 = d
4 = e
5 = f
6 = h
7 = i
8 = k
9 = l
10 = n
11 = o
12 = r
13 = s
14 = t
15 = w
16 = y

1. _____
   14 - 12 - 16

2. _____
   5 - 12 - 16

3. _____
   14 - 6 - 7 - 10 - 8

4. _____
   14 - 12 - 4 - 4

5. _____
   15 - 6 - 4 - 12 - 4

6. _____
   3 - 12 - 16

7. _____
   2 - 12 - 16

8. _____
   15 - 6 - 16

9. _____
   5 - 9 - 16

10. _____
    15 - 6 - 1 - 14

11. _____
    15 - 6 - 11

12. _____
    13 - 8 - 16

Spelling Words

try	cry	dry	fry
sky	fly	tree	think
what	who	why	where

E. Using Other Word Forms

Change the *y* to *i* and add *es* to each spelling word.
Write the new word for each sentence.

1. cry – y + ies   Sometimes the baby _____ .

2. sky – y + ies   Clouds fill the _____ above.

3. fry – y + ies   The cook _____ potatoes.

4. dry – y + ies   Father _____ the dishes.

5. try – y + ies   The baby _____ to walk.

6. fly – y + ies   The bird _____ above the trees.

F. Rhyme Words

Write the spelling words that rhyme.

    think   tree   what   where   who   why

1. do, _____   4. there, _____

2. but, _____   5. sky, _____

3. me, _____   6. pink, _____

G. Word Change

Write a spelling word in place of the underlined words
in each sentence. Check your answers in the
Glossary/SPELLEX®.

1. There are stars in the space above the earth. _____

2. Do you know in what place my jacket is? _____

3. The storm knocked the tall plant down. _____

4. We heard the loud call of some animal. _____

5. Tell me for what reason you are late. _____

6. I will work hard to do well in school. _____

7. Do you know what person that is? _____

8. Jets move through the air quickly. _____

9. We will cook in hot oil the fish. _____

10. I know which thing I want. _____

11. Our clothes are not wet. _____

12. I have to use my mind. _____

H. I Know My Words. Test your words.

A. Time to Test. Test your words.

B. Words   **Shapes**   **Write**

1. sea   _____

2. meat   _____

3. each   _____

4. clean   _____

5. leave   _____

6. seed   _____

7. keep   _____

8. feel   _____

9. sleeping   _____

10. road   _____

11. boat   _____

12. coat   _____

C. Words in Sentences

Fish live in the **sea**.
We ate the **meat**.
Give one to **each** person.
My hands are **clean**.
They will **leave** now.
The flower grew from a **seed**.

You can **keep** the toy.
Does the stone **feel** smooth?
The baby is **sleeping**.
The **road** was long.
The **boat** is fast.
Wear a warm **coat**.

D. *Ea* and *Ee* Words

Use the clues to write the *ee* and *ea* spelling words.

ee

1. I don't _____ well.

2. not give away, but _____

3. You plant this.

4. not <u>waking</u>, but _____

ea

5. to go away

6. not <u>fish</u>, but _____

7. You swim in this.

8. not <u>dirty</u>, but _____

9. Tell _____ of us the story.

Spelling Words

sea	meat	each	clean
leave	seed	keep	feel
sleeping	road	boat	coat

E. Crossword Puzzle

Use the clues to write three spelling words in the puzzle.

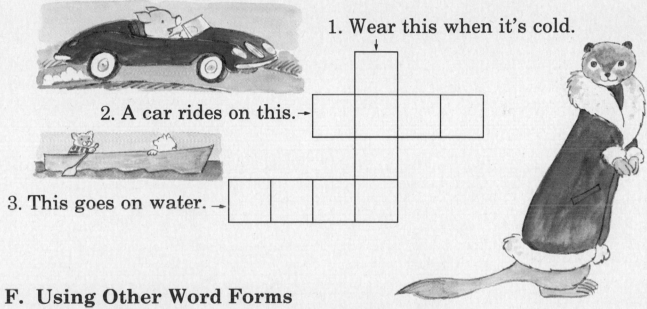

1. Wear this when it's cold.

2. A car rides on this. →

3. This goes on water. →

F. Using Other Word Forms

Circle these words hidden in the word-worm.
Write the words.

boats   kept   roads   seeds   felt   meats   seas   slept

gmeatsckeptsjseedspnxsleptdfeltjsuboatsnseasfroads

1. _____   4. _____   7. _____

2. _____   5. _____   8. _____

3. _____   6. _____

G. Missing Vowels

Find the missing vowels *ea, ee,* or *oa* for each word.
Then write the spelling word.

ea

1. __ __ ch   _____

2. s __ __   _____

3. l __ __ ve   _____

4. cl __ __ n   _____

5. m __ __ t   _____

ee

6. k __ __ p   _____

7. s __ __ d   _____

8. f __ __ l   _____

9. sl __ __ ping   _____

oa

10. b __ __ t   _____

11. r __ __ d   _____

12. c __ __ t   _____

H. I Know My Words. Test your words.

A. Word Math

Follow the signs to write new words. For words that end in *y*, change the *y* to *i* before adding *es*.

1. camp + ing = _____

2. clean + ed = _____

3. wish + es = _____

4. open + ed = _____

5. jumped – ed = _____

6. need + ing = _____

7. cool + ing = _____

8. dip + s = _____

9. city – y + ies = _____

10. fly – y + ies = _____

11. try – y + ies = _____

12. fry – y + ies = _____

13. sky – y + ies = _____

14. cry – y + ies = _____

15. dry – y + ies = _____

B. Crossword Puzzle

Add *s* or *es* to the spelling words to complete the puzzle.
When a word ends in *ch,* like *beach* and *lunch,* add *es.*

band	coat	log	room	tree
beach	home	lunch	seed	week
boat	lamp	road	son	zoo

Across

1. not bushes
3. drums in _____
4. places to find shells
6. You burn them in a fire.
7. sandwiches for _____
9. These have four walls.
11. Plants grow from these.
13. not jackets

Down

2. streets
3. small ships
5. not daughters
7. They give off light.
8. places where people live
10. They have seven days.
12. places to see animals

120

C. Sentence Fun
Complete the sentences with these words. Use the number clues.

1	2	3	4	5
leaving	sleeps	slept	hits	be
kept	died	feeding	foot	thinking
sooner	greener	found	knows	feels

1. The mail came (1) _____ today than yesterday.

2. Father (1) _____ his promise to us.

3. What time are you (1) _____ for school?

4. The flowers (2) _____ because they needed water.

5. My eyes are (2) _____ than yours.

6. Our dog (2) _____ on a mat every night.

7. The zoo keeper is (3) _____ the animals.

8. I (3) _____ well last night.

9. Have you (3) _____ your lost ring yet?

10. Who (4) _____ how to draw a cat?

11. My friend (4) _____ the ball hard.

12. Can you hop on one (4) _____ ?

13. I have been (5) _____ about you.

14. The water (5) _____ so cold!

15. Mother will (5) _____ waiting for us.

D. Unscramble

Use the letters to write a spelling word for each sentence.

bath	by	from	sea	where
boots	each	meat	too	who
both	food	noon	what	why

1. ywh   Do you know _____ the baby is crying?

2. owh   Did you see _____ dropped this glove?

3. echa   Grandmother gave _____ of us a ball.

4. oonn   We are going on a picnic at _____ .

5. dfoo   We need to go shopping for _____ .

6. mtea   We had _____ and corn for dinner.

7. eas   I would like to live by the _____ !

8. reewh Please ask _____ the bus stop is.

9. yb   I like to sit _____ the window.

10. oto   Your friend may come _____ .

11. thba Let's give the baby a _____ !

12. mofr What town are you _____ ?

13. othb Wash _____ pairs of socks.

14. twha Tell me _____ the date is.

15. soobt My new _____ are black.

A. Time to Test. Test your words.

B. Words	Shapes	Write
1. bread		_____
2. read		_____
3. sled		_____
4. left		_____
5. soft		_____
6. flat		_____
7. bang		_____
8. bring		_____
9. king		_____
10. into		_____
11. oh		_____
12. of		_____

C. Words in Sentences

The birds ate some **bread.**
I **read** my book.
Our **sled** is red.
I write with my **left** hand.
Is the pillow **soft**?
Our backyard is **flat.**

We heard a **bang.**
I'll **bring** the game with me.
The **king** rules the land.
The cat went **into** the house.
Oh, no!
I drank a glass **of** milk.

D. Word Change

Write spelling words in place of the underlined words in the sentences. Check your answers in the **Glossary/SPELLEX**®.

1. My, cry of surprise my! You frightened me! _____

2. We baked food made from flour and milk. _____

3. Don't make loud noises with the drums. _____

4. They went away from here a while ago. _____

5. Please carry this gift to your mother. _____

6. I looked at and understood the book. _____

7. We live in a house made from stone. _____

8. Our object to ride over snow is fast! _____

9. The prince's father is a kind ruler. _____

10. The road is smooth and even. _____

11. Put the shoes inside the box. _____

12. My bed is not hard. _____

Spelling Words

bread	read	sled	left
soft	flat	bang	bring
king	into	oh	of

E. Using Other Word Forms

Use the clues to write these words in the blanks.
Then use the boxed letters to write a hidden word.

banging	bringing	kings	sleds
breads	flatter	reading	softer

1. My hands are soft,
   but yours are _____ . _ _ _ _ _ _ ☐

2. smoother _ _ _ _ _ ☐ _

3. We baked many _____ . _ _ _ ☐ _ _

4. one sled, two _____ _ _ _ ☐ _

5. not taking _ _ _ ☐ _

6. men who rule countries _ _ ☐ _ _

7. Drums are for _____ . _ ☐ _ _ _ _ _

HIDDEN WORD: not writing, but _ _ _ _ _ _ _

F. Story Time
Complete the story with the spelling words. Use the number clues.

1	2	3	4
bring	sled	soft	bang
flat	read	into	Oh
king	of	bread	left

There once was a (1) _____ who had a birthday.

People came to (1) _____ him gifts. His mother

brought him a thin, (1) _____ book. He

(2) _____ it right away. His daughter brought him a

(2) _____ for sliding. The cook brought him a big loaf

(2) _____ wheat (3) _____ . Later the

king's son came (3) _____ his room. He told the king

to put two (3) _____ pillows over his ears. Then the

son (4) _____ to go outside. There was a big

(4) _____ . Bright lights and pretty colors fell from

the sky. The king said, "(4) _____ ! That was the best

birthday gift of all!" What was the son's gift to his father?

G. I Know My Words. Test your words.

Lesson 32

A. Time to Test. Test your words.

B. Words   **Shapes**   **Write**

1. ant

2. plan

3. than

4. stand

5. trip

6. milk

7. shop

8. drop

9. stop

10. spot

11. much

12. shut

C. Words in Sentences

An **ant** ran across my shoe.
Let's make a **plan**.
My sister is bigger **than** I.
Please **stand** straight.
We took a long **trip**.
Would you like **milk** or cream?

Let's **shop** together.
I felt a **drop** of rain.
They will **stop** and rest.
Look for a picnic **spot**.
I ate too **much**!
Please **shut** the door.

D. Clues

Use the clues to write the spelling words.

1. My brother is smaller _____ I.

2. You do this in a store. _____

3. Silk rhymes with _____ .

4. a small mark or _____

5. not pick up, but _____

6. not a little, but _____

7. not open, but _____

8. You go on a _____ .

9. Brakes _____ a car.

10. a tiny bug or _____

11. not sit, but _____

12. an idea or _____

128

Spelling Words

ant	plan	than	stand
trip	milk	shop	drop
stop	spot	much	shut

E. Think Time
Write a sentence that uses the two spelling words.

1. stop, trip _____

_____

2. milk, shop _____

_____

3. spot, stand _____

_____

4. ant, than _____

_____

5. much, plan _____

_____

6. drop, shut _____

_____

F. Using Other Word Forms

Double the final consonant and add *ed* or *ing* to the spelling words.

	+ ed	+ ing
1. stop + p	_____	_____
2. shop + p	_____	_____
3. drop + p	_____	_____
4. plan + n	_____	_____
5. trip + p	_____	_____
6. spot + t	_____	_____

G. Word-Worm

Circle these words hidden in the word-worm.
Write the words.

ant   milk   much   shut   stand   than

1. _____   3. _____   5. _____

2. _____   4. _____   6. _____

H. I Know My Words. Test your words.

A. Time to Test. Test your words.

B. Words	Shapes	Write

1. flag _____

2. glad _____

3. grab _____

4. stamp _____

5. child _____

6. thin _____

7. train _____

8. plays _____

9. any _____

10. many _____

11. coming _____

12. new _____

C. Words in Sentences

They will wave the **flag**.
I'll be **glad** to help.
We will **grab** the rope.
Remember to lick the **stamp**.
I am an only **child**.
My arms are **thin**.

They rode on a **train**.
My dog **plays** in the snow.
Do you have **any** pets?
We have **many** toys.
Who is **coming** with us?
We have a **new** bat.

D. Clues

Use the clues to write the spelling words.

1. When you take hold quickly, you _____ .

2. The team _____ football in the field.

3. To mail a letter, you need a _____ .

4. Our _____ is red, white, and blue.

5. The opposite of going is _____ .

6. The opposite of sad is _____ .

7. The opposite of old is _____ .

8. The opposite of fat is _____ .

9. A young person is a _____ .

10. You take trips on a _____ .

11. A lot of things are _____ .

12. Is there _____ milk?

Spelling Words

flag	glad	grab	stamp
child	thin	train	plays
any	many	coming	new

E. Hidden Words

Find the spelling words hidden in this puzzle.
The words go down and across. Circle and write each word.

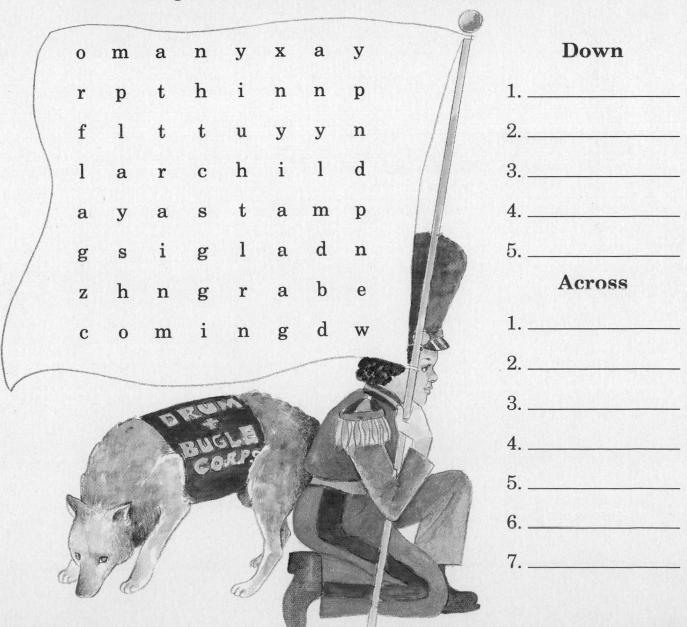

```
o  m  a  n  y  x  a  y
r  p  t  h  i  n  n  p
f  l  t  t  u  y  y  n
l  a  r  c  h  i  l  d
a  y  a  s  t  a  m  p
g  s  i  g  l  a  d  n
z  h  n  g  r  a  b  e
c  o  m  i  n  g  d  w
```

Down

1. _____
2. _____
3. _____
4. _____
5. _____

Across

1. _____
2. _____
3. _____
4. _____
5. _____
6. _____
7. _____

F. Using Other Word Forms
Complete the sentences with these words.

children   grabbed   stamps
flags   playing   trains

1. My sister is _____ with her blocks.

2. We will ride on two _____ .

3. The dog _____ the rope with its teeth.

4. There are _____ hanging in the classrooms.

5. I need some _____ to mail my letters.

6. The _____ are drawing pictures.

G. Letter Scramble
Use the letters to write a spelling word.

1. g f l a

2. n a i t r

3. i c h l d

4. w n e

5. d g l a

6. a b g r

7. m o c i n g

8. n y a m

9. m p s t a

10. i t h n

11. a y p l s

12. y n a

H. I Know My Words. Test your words.

Lesson 34

A. Time to Test. Test your words.

B. Words	**Shapes**	**Write**
1. old		_____
2. sold		_____
3. hold		_____
4. cold		_____
5. told		_____
6. fold		_____
7. wash		_____
8. ask		_____
9. back		_____
10. black		_____
11. blue		_____
12. white		_____

C. Words in Sentences

They are my **old** friends.
I **sold** my bike.
Please **hold** my hand.
The ice is **cold**.
You never **told** me your name.
Please **fold** your paper in half.

Dad will **wash** the dishes.
We will **ask** them.
I am in **back** of you.
The tar is **black**.
My eyes are **blue**.
Snow is **white**.

D. Find the Words

Write each spelling word in the correct group.
One word will be used twice.

Words With <u>old</u>

_____   _____

_____   _____

_____   _____

Words With <u>sk</u>, <u>ck</u>, <u>sh</u>

_____   _____

Color Words

_____

_____

_____

136

Spelling Words

old	sold	hold	cold
told	fold	wash	ask
back	black	blue	white

E. Story Time

Complete the story with the spelling words. Use the number clues.

1	2	3	4
wash	old	sold	black
cold	ask	told	back
blue	hold	white	fold

One (1) _____ , windy day I went to hang my

(1) _____ out to dry. The sky was (1) _____

and the sun was shining. I decided to (2) _____ an

(2) _____ friend to help me. She wanted to

(2) _____ my basket of clothes while I hung them.

I (3) _____ her about the store that (3) _____

me my (3) _____ shirt with the (4) _____

stripes. Later she helped me (4) _____ the clothes.

Then we went (4) _____ to the store to buy her a shirt!

F. Using Other Word Forms

Add *er* and *est* to each spelling word. Drop the final *e* before adding *er* or *est* to the words *white* and *blue*.

	+ er	+ est
1. cold	_____	_____
2. old	_____	_____
3. black	_____	_____
4. white – e	_____	_____
5. blue – e	_____	_____

G. Unscramble

Use the underlined letters to write a spelling word.

1. Please remember to <u>ldof</u> your clothes. _____

2. Grandfather <u>osld</u> his stamps. _____

3. Will you <u>hldo</u> the door open for me? _____

4. My room is in the <u>ackb</u> of the house. _____

5. Did you <u>ska</u> your parents if you can go? _____

6. Our teacher <u>ldto</u> us a new story. _____

7. Please <u>shwa</u> your face and hands. _____

H. I Know My Words. Test your words.

138

Lesson 35

A. Time to Test. Test your words.

B. Words   **Shapes**   **Write**

1. talk _____

2. state _____

3. paper _____

4. warm _____

5. mark _____

6. part _____

7. list _____

8. write _____

9. rose _____

10. sometimes _____

11. help _____

12. bedtime _____

C. Words in Sentences

I want to **talk** to you.

What **state** do you live in?

We need some writing **paper**.

Give the baby **warm** milk.

The teacher will **mark** our tests.

Which **part** did you read?

Make a **list** of things you need.

I will **write** you a letter.

A **rose** smells sweet.

We stay up late **sometimes**.

Please **help** me!

Tell us a **bedtime** story!

D. Word Change

Write spelling words in place of the underlined words in the sentences. Check your answers in the **Glossary/SPELLEX®**.

1. The teacher passed out <u>something to write on</u>. _____

2. What <u>part of the United States</u> are you from? _____

3. The bath water is <u>not very hot but not cool</u>. _____

4. I will <u>give aid to</u> you with your homework. _____

5. We picked a <u>flower that grows on a bush</u>. _____

6. Add milk to the grocery <u>group of things</u>. _____

7. I will <u>make up a letter</u> to you next week. _____

8. Did you <u>speak</u> to your friend today? _____

9. It is almost <u>time for sleep at night</u>. _____

10. We walk to school <u>now and then</u>. _____

11. May I have <u>some</u> of your apple? _____

12. Did the ink leave a <u>spot</u>? _____

Spelling Words

talk	state	paper	warm
mark	part	list	write
rose	sometimes	help	bedtime

E. Think Time
Write a sentence that uses the two spelling words.

1. list, write _____

_____

2. paper, mark _____

_____

3. bedtime, warm _____

_____

4. part, state _____

_____

5. talk, sometimes _____

_____

6. rose, help _____

_____

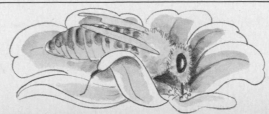

F. Using Other Word Forms
Complete the sentences with these words. Use the number clues.

1	2	3	4
bedtimes	marked	roses	warmest
helps	papers	states	writing
lists	parts	talks	

1. Today was the (4) _____ day of the week.

2. Mother (1) _____ me with my homework.

3. My little sister (3) _____ a lot now.

4. We study (1) _____ of spelling words.

5. The United States has 50 (3) _____ .

6. The teacher (2) _____ our papers.

7. We drew lines on our (2) _____ .

8. Smell the pretty red (3) _____ .

9. We have early (1) _____ .

10. A car has many (2) _____ .

11. I am (4) _____ a letter.

G. I Know My Words. Test your words.

A. More Than One
Add *s* to the spelling words in each pair.
Write both words.

1. state
   flag

   The fifty _____ have different

   _____ .

2. sled
   back

   We carried our _____ on our

   _____ .

3. ant
   rose

   Some _____ are crawling on the

   _____ .

4. king
   stamp

   Do _____ use _____ to mail
   their letters?

5. paper
   mark

   These _____ have red _____
   on them.

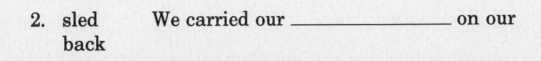

Write the word that means more than one child.
Use the **Glossary/SPELLEX®**.   _____

B. Add *s*
Add *s* to each spelling word in the
sentence. Write the new word.

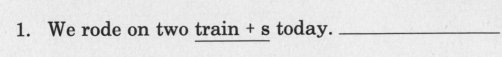

1. We rode on two <u>train</u> + s today. _____

2. Mother <u>read</u> + s to us every night. _____

3. That man <u>sell</u> + s balloons. _____

4. This book has four different <u>part</u> + s. _____

C. *Er* and *Est*

Add *er* or *est* to the underlined word in each sentence.
Double the final consonant before adding *er* or *est*
to *flat* and *thin*.

1. Which tire is <u>flat</u> + t + er? _____

2. Winter is <u>cold</u> + er than summer. _____

3. My bike is <u>new</u> + er than my sister's. _____

4. My brother has the <u>thin</u> + n + est legs! _____

5. I am one week <u>old</u> + er than my friend. _____

6. Mom's coat is made of the <u>soft</u> + est wool. _____

7. The weather is <u>warm</u> + er today than yesterday. _____

D. Hidden Words

Find these words hidden in the puzzle.
The words go across and down. Circle and write each word.

brought   leaving   stood
gladly   playing   wrote
held   breads

```
l  s  o  w  r  o  t  e
e  p  l  a  y  i  n  g
a  s  t  o  o  d  x  q
v  b  r  o  u  g  h  t
i  a  d  i  k  t  n  o
n  b  r  e  a  d  s  p
g  j  k  r  h  e  l  d
g  l  a  d  l  y  s  t
```

Across

1. _____

2. _____

3. _____

4. _____

5. _____

6. _____

7. _____

Down

1. _____

E. Making Changes

Add *ed* and *ing* to the spelling words.
When a word ends with one vowel and one consonant,
double the consonant before adding *ed* or *ing*.

		+ ed	+ ing
1.	bang	_____	_____
2.	ask	_____	_____
3.	milk	_____	_____
4.	wash	_____	_____
5.	talk	_____	_____
6.	fold	_____	_____
7.	help	_____	_____
8.	list	_____	_____
9.	spot + t	_____	_____
10.	plan + n	_____	_____
11.	trip + p	_____	_____
12.	shop + p	_____	_____
13.	drop + p	_____	_____
14.	stop + p	_____	_____
15.	grab + b	_____	_____

F. Sentence Fun

Complete the sentences with these spelling words.
Use the number clues.

1	2	3	4	5
than	white	shut	blue	bedtime
many	much	into	sometimes	black
any	of	told	Oh	coming

1. The Farmer in the Dell has so (1) _____ animals.

2. Baa-Baa Black Sheep, have you (1) _____ wool?

3. The giant is taller (1) _____ Jack.

4. "This bed is (2) _____ too hard!" said Goldilocks.

5. Have you ever heard (2) _____ Little Boy Blue?

6. Color Frosty the Snowman (2) _____ .

7. The wolf (3) _____ Red Riding Hood many lies.

8. Snow White bit (3) _____ the bad apple.

9. The Three Pigs (3) _____ the door on the wolf.

10. "(4) _____ !" cried Baby Bear. "Someone's in my bed!"

11. Did a piece of (4) _____ sky fall on Chicken Little?

12. The Three Bears (4) _____ went for long walks.

13. Are Jack and Jill (5) _____ down the hill?

14. Mother Goose wrote (5) _____ stories.

15. Frosty's eyes are as (5) _____ as coal.

SPELLEX® Glossary
Level B

This part of your spelling book is called **SPELLEX® Glossary— Level B.** It lists all the spelling words from **Working Words in Spelling—Level B.** The **SPELLEX®** Glossary can help you as you do other schoolwork. The **SPELLEX®** Glossary has many of the words you will need to write every day. You can use the **SPELLEX®** Glossary to check the spellings and meanings of these important writing words.

The **SPELLEX®** Glossary is easy to use. All the spelling words appear in alphabetical order. Each spelling word is printed in dark letters. If the spelling word is not a base word, you are told what the base word is. The meaning of the base word is also given. After the base word and its meaning, other forms of the spelling word are given.

Here are the different parts of the **SPELLEX®** Glossary entries:

base word — go |gō| *v.* To move from one place to another: *We will go to the movies with you.* **goes, went,** — *other word forms* **going, gone**

respelling ————————— *part of speech*

spelling word — **goes** |gōz| *v.* Moves from one place — *meaning* to another: *The bus goes to New* — *sample sentence* *York every day.* [see *go*] ———— *base word*

SPELLEX®—a registered trademark of Curriculum Associates, Inc.
SPELLEX® Glossary incorporated by permission of Curriculum Associates, Inc.

Pronunciation Key

ă	pat	ô	alter, caught, for, paw
ā	aid, fey, pay	oi	boy, noise, oil
â	air, care, wear	ou	cow, out
ä	father	ŏŏ	took
b	bib	ōō	boot, fruit
ch	church	p	pop
d	deed	r	roar
ĕ	pet, pleasure	s	miss, sauce, see
ē	be, bee, easy, leisure	sh	dish, ship
f	fast, fife, off, phase, rough	t	tight
g	gag	th	path, thin
h	hat	*th*	bathe, this
hw	which	ŭ	cut, rough
ĭ	pit	û	circle, firm, heard,
ī	by, guy, pie		term, turn, urge, word
î	dear, deer, fierce, mere	v	cave, valve, vine
j	judge	w	with
k	cat, kick, pique	y	yes
l	lid, needle	yōō	abuse, use
m	am, man, mum	z	rose, size, xylophone, zebra
n	no, sudden	zh	garage, pleasure, vision
ng	thing	ə	about, silent, pencil,
ŏ	horrible, pot		lemon, circus
ō	go, hoarse, row, toe	ər	butter

STRESS
Primary stress ′ bi·ol′o·gy |bī ŏl′ə jē|
Secondary stress ′ bi′o·log′i·cal |bī′ə lŏj′ĭ kəl|

A

add |ăd| *v.* To find how many two or more numbers make together: *Add 2 and 2 to get 4.* **adds, added, adding, addition**

ago |ə gō′| *adj.* Before now or in the past: *A long time ago I planted these blue and yellow flowers.*

ant |ănt| *n.* A small black or red insect that lives in the ground or in wood: *This ant is small and black.* **ants**

any |ĕn′ē| *adj.* **1.** One of a group of three or more: *Use any pencil.* **2.** Some: *I don't have any sisters.*

apple |ăp′əl| *n.* A round fruit that is red, yellow, or green: *I have a green apple.* **apples**

are |är| *v.* **1.** To do something: *We are walking slowly.* **2.** To be: *We are happy.* [see *be*]

arm |ärm| *n.* The part of the body between the shoulder and the hand: *I hurt my arm when I fell.* **arms**

ask |ăsk| *v.* To say as a question: *Ask her if she found my hat.* **asks, asked, asking**

ate |āt| *v.* Chewed and swallowed food: *I ate the last apple.* [see *eat*]

B

baby |bā′bē| *n.* A very young child: *The baby is sleeping.* **babies**

back |băk| *n.* The side opposite the front: *Look in the back of the book.* *adv.* To a place you've been to before: *We're going back to my cousins' house next week.* **backs**

bad |băd| *adj.* **1.** Terrible: *We had a bad storm last night.* **2.** Naughty: *The bad grey cat scratched me.* **3.** Upsetting: *We heard bad news about a plane crash.* **badly, badness**

bake |bāk| *v.* To cook food in an oven: *I will bake a pie.* **bakes, baked, baking, baker**

band |bănd| *n.* A group of people who play music: *My brother plays the drums in a rock band.* **bands**

bang |băng| *n.* A sudden, loud noise: *The cans fell with a bang.* *v.* To make a sudden, loud noise: *I like to bang the drums.* **bangs, banged, banging**

bark |bärk| *n.* **1.** The sound a dog makes: *That bark came from my dog.* **2.** The outside covering of a tree: *The bark on that tree is brown.* *v.* To make a noise like a dog: *Those dogs will bark at the neighbors.* **barks, barked, barking**

barn |bärn| *n.* A building used to store hay and grain. A barn can also be a place where animals live: *The barn is filled with horses.* **barns**

bath |băth| *n.* The water in a tub used for washing. *My bath is ready.* **baths**

be |bē| *v.* To take up or hold a certain place or position: *I will be there.* **am, is, are, was, were, been, being**

beach |bēch| *n.* The land close to the water that is covered with sand: *We played in the sand at the beach.* **beaches**

bedtime |bĕd′tīm′| *n.* Time for sleep at night: *My bedtime is nine o'clock.* **bedtimes**

been |bĭn| *v.* Took up or held a certain position: *We have been here all day.* [see *be*]

bell |bĕl| *n.* A metal cup that makes a ringing sound: *Each bell has a different sound.* **bells**

beside |bĭ sīd′| *prep.* Next to: *They stood beside the door.*

best |bĕst| *adj.* **1.** Most liked: *I miss my best friend.* **2.** Most good: *This is the best book I've ever read.* **better**

ă pat / ā pay / â care / ä father / ĕ pet / ē be / ĭ pit / ī pie / î fierce / ŏ pot / ō go / ô paw, for / oi oil / o͝o book / o͞o boot / ou out / ŭ cut / û fur / *th* the / th thin / hw which / zh vision / ə ago, item, pencil, atom, circus
Key—©1977 by Houghton Mifflin Company. Reprinted by permission from THE AMERICAN HERITAGE SCHOOL DICTIONARY.

bet |bĕt| *n.* A promise between two people who think differently about some matter. They agree that the one who is wrong will give something to the one who is right: *They made a bet about who will win the soccer game.* *v.* To be very sure about something: *I bet you go to the game.* ***bets, betting***

better |bĕt'ər| *adj.* Feeling less ill: *I am better today.* *adv.* In a more excellent way: *You write better than I.* [see *best*]

bird |bûrd| *n.* An animal with feathers, two legs, and wings: *The bird built a nest.* ***birds***

bite |bīt| *v.* To cut into with teeth: *The dog won't bite you.* ***bites, biting, bit, bitten, biter***

black |blăk| *adj.* The darkest color. *Black* is the opposite of *white: The black crow sat on the fence.* ***blacker, blackest***

block |blŏk| *n.* An object with six sides that are shaped like squares. A block can be made of wood, ice, stone, or other things: *Put one block on top.* ***blocks, blocked, blocking***

blow |blō| *v.* To send a strong, rush of air: *The wind will blow the curtains.* —**Blow out**—To put out by blowing. ***blows, blew, blowing, blown, blower***

blue |blo͞o| *adj.* The color of the sky on a clear day: *The blue boat is sinking.* ***bluer, bluest***

boat |bōt| *n.* A small ship that carries people and things over water: *Our boat is filled with fish.* ***boats, boating***

boot |bo͞ot| *n.* A tall shoe that fits over the foot and part of the leg: *I pulled my boot over my ankle.* ***boots***

boots |bo͞ots| *n.* More than one boot: *You must wear your boots in the snow.* [see *boot*]

both |bōth| *adj.* Each of two: *Both brothers will go to the party.* *pron.* The two together: *Both of them live here.*

box |bŏks| *n.* A case with four sides and a bottom. It is used to hold things: *The box is in the closet.* ***boxes, boxed, boxing, boxer***

bread |brĕd| *n.* A food made from flour, which is mixed with milk or water and then baked: *This bread is made from corn.* **breads**

bring |brĭng| *v.* To take someone or carry something from one place to another: *Bring the food to the table.* **brings, bringing, brought**

brother |brŭ*th*′ər| *n.* A boy or a man with the same parents as someone else: *My brother will meet us at the movie theater.* **brothers**

bug |bŭg| *n.* An insect like a bee or a fly: *There is a bug on that flower.* **bugs**

bunny |bŭn′ē| n. A rabbit: *The scared bunny hopped away.* **bunnies**

bus |bŭs| *n.* A large machine with many seats for carrying people: *We waited for the bus.* **buses**

butter |bŭt′ər| *n.* A fat made from cream: *We made butter at home.* **butters, buttered, buttering**

by |bī| *prep.* Near: *Those flowers grow by the lake.*

C

cake |kāk| *n.* A sweet food. A cake is made from flour, sugar, milk and eggs and baked in an oven: *The cake is in the oven.* **cakes**

call |kôl| *v.* **1.** To speak to on the telephone: *I'll call you tonight.* **2.** To speak to in a loud voice, to shout: *Call for help.* **calls, called, calling, caller**

came |kām| *v.* Arrived at a place: *They came home from their trip.* [see *come*]

ă pat / ā pay / â care / ä father / ĕ pet / ē be / ĭ pit / ī pie / î fierce / ŏ pot / ō go / ô paw, for / oi oil / ŏŏ book / ōō boot / ou out / ŭ cut / û fur / *th* the / th thin / hw which / zh vision / ə ago, item, pencil, atom, circus Key—©1977 by Houghton Mifflin Company. Reprinted by permission from THE AMERICAN HERITAGE SCHOOL DICTIONARY.

camp |kămp| *v.* To live outdoors: *We will camp in the park near the lake. n.* An outdoor area where people live for a time in tents, trailers, or cabins: *Our camp is near a lake.* **camps, camped, camping, camper**

candy |kăn′dē| *n.* A sweet food made mostly with sugar: *This candy is filled with nuts.* **candies**

cap |kăp| *n.* A small hat that fits the head closely: *My baseball cap is blue.* **caps**

car |kär| *n.* A machine for carrying people. It has four wheels, an engine, seats, and windows: *Our car has only two doors.* **cars**

card |kärd| *n.* A small, stiff piece of paper often folded in half: *This birthday card is from my uncle.* **cards**

cart |kärt| *n.* A wooden wagon with two wheels, used to carry heavy loads. A cart is usually pulled by a strong animal: *The cart belongs to the farmer.* **carts**

child |chīld| *n.* A young boy or girl: *The child was looking for the lost dog.* **children, childish**

city |sĭt′ē| *n.* A large town where many people live and work: *We are going shopping in the city.* **cities**

clap |klăp| *v.* To hit both hands together loudly: *We clap our hands to the music. n.* A sharp, sudden sound: *We heard a loud clap, and then it began to rain.* **claps, clapped, clapping**

clean |klēn| *adj.* Neat and without dirt: *Sit at the clean table.* **cleans, cleaned, cleaning, cleaner, cleanest**

clock |klŏk| *n.* A machine that measures time: *Look at the clock and tell me the time.* **clocks**

coat |kōt| *n.* A long and heavy kind of clothing worn over other clothes: *My wool coat is blue.* **coats**

cold |kōld| *adj.* Not having warmth or heat: *This cold fruit tastes good.* **colder, coldest, colds**

come |kŭm| *v.* **1.** To arrive at a place: *Come home by six o'clock.* **2.** To move toward: *Come closer to me.* **comes, came, coming**

coming |kŭm'ĭng| *v.* Arriving at a place: *Mother is coming at noon.* [see come]

cook |kŏŏk| *v.* To make food by using heat: *I will cook dinner tonight.* **cooks, cooked, cooking**

cool |kŏŏl| *adj.* Not warm but not quite cold: *On cool days I wear my wool coat.* **cools, cooled, cooling, cooler, coolest**

corn |kôrn| *n.* A vegetable that grows on a tall, green plant: *We had corn for dinner.*

cry |krī| *v.* To have tears fall from the eyes, while feeling unhappy: *Many people cry at sad movies.* *n.* A loud call: *We heard the cry of a wolf.* **cries, cried, crying, crier**

D

dark |därk| *adj.* Without light or brightness: *The sky became dark before the storm.* *n.* A time or place without light: *I went to the store before dark.* **darker, darkest, darken, darkness**

dear |dîr| *adj.* Much loved. *This is my dear sister.* **dearer, dearest**

den |dĕn| *n.* **1.** A room used for study or play: *The TV is in the den.* **2.** A home for some wild animals: *The bears' den is a cave.* **dens**

die |dī| *v.* To stop living: *The plants will die without water and sunshine.* **dies, died, dying**

dinner |dĭn'ər| *n.* The biggest meal of the day: *Please have dinner at our house on Sunday.* **dinners**

ă pat / ā pay / â care / ä father / ĕ pet / ē be / ĭ pit / ī pie / î fierce / ŏ pot / ō go / ô paw, for / oi oil / ŏŏ book / ōō boot / ou out / ŭ cut / û fur / *th* the / th thin / hw which / zh vision / ə ago, item, pencil, atom, circus
Key—©1977 by Houghton Mifflin Company. Reprinted by permission from THE AMERICAN HERITAGE SCHOOL DICTIONARY.

dip |dĭp| *v.* To put part of something in a liquid for a moment: *I will dip my hand in water.* **dips, dipped, dipping**

dish |dĭsh| *n.* A plate or bowl used to hold food: *I ate a dish of nuts after dinner.* **dishes**

do |do͞o| *v.* To start and finish: *I will do my homework after school.* **does, did, done, doing**

doll |dŏl| *n.* A toy that looks like a person, often a baby: *The rag doll has red hair.* **dolls**

done |dŭn| *v.* Finished: *They have done the dishes.* [see *do*]

door |dôr| *n.* The part of a room or building that you open or close to enter or leave: *The door is closed.* **doors**

dot |dŏt| *n.* A small, round spot, or a point: *The dot on the map shows where I live.* **dots, dotted, dotting**

down |doun| *prep.* From a higher place to a lower place: *The boat sailed down the river.*

dress |drĕs| *v.* To put on clothes: *Dress quickly.* —**Dress up**—To put on nice clothes. **dresses, dressed, dressing, dresser, dressy**

drop |drŏp| *n.* A small bit of liquid: *I felt a drop of rain. v.* To fall or let fall from a higher to a lower place: *Don't drop the new vase.* **drops, dropped, dropping**

dry |drī| *adj.* Without water: *The dry plants need watering.* **dries, dried, drying, drier, driest**

duck |dŭk| *n.* A water bird with a flat bill and webbed feet: *The duck swam quickly.* **ducks**

dust |dŭst| *n.* Very tiny pieces of dirt: *There is dust on the top of the table.* **dusts, dusted, dusting, duster, dusty**

E

each |ēch| *n.* Every one: *Each of the students has a pen.*

eat |ēt| *v.* To chew and swallow food: *I will eat lunch soon.* **eats, ate, eaten, eating, eater**

end |ĕnd| *n.* The place where a thing stops; the last part: *Today we will read the end of the story.* **ends, ended, ending**

even |ē′vən| *adj.* **1.** Not odd. *Even numbers can be divided exactly by 2. The numbers 2, 4, and 6 are even.* **2.** The same or equal: *I put the pennies into two even piles.* **evens, evened, evening, evenly**

ever |ĕv′ər| *adv.* At any time: *Have you ever climbed to the top of a mountain?*

every |ĕv′rē| *adj.* All; each one: *We saw every room in the huge house.*

eye |ī| *n.* One of the two parts of the face that a person or animal sees with: *My left eye is weak.* **eyes**

eyes |īz| *n.* The two parts of the face that a person or animal sees with: *Close your eyes and make a wish.* [see *eye*]

F

fall |fôl| *v.* To drop or come down from a higher place: *The leaves fall from the trees in October.* **falls, fell, falling, fallen**

fan |făn| *n.* A machine that blows air around: *We used a fan to keep ourselves cool.* **fans, fanned, fanning**

far |fär| *adj.* Not near: *My desk is at the far corner of the room.*

farm |färm| *n.* A piece of land where food is grown and animals are raised: *We grow corn on our farm.* **farms, farmed, farming, farmer**

fast |făst| *adv.* Quickly: *How fast can you get here? adj.* Quick: *Squirrels are fast climbers.* **faster, fastest**

father |fä′thər| *n.* A male parent: *My father has two brothers.* **fathers**

fed |fĕd| *v.* Gave food to a person or animal to eat: *I fed the cat.* [see *feed*]

feed |fēd| *v.* To give food to a person or animal to eat: *I will feed the baby.* **feeds, fed, feeding**

feel |fēl| *v.* **1.** To touch: *We like to feel the cat's soft fur.* **2.** To have a sense of: *They feel sick.* **feels, felt, feeling**

feet |fēt| *n.* More than one foot: *A duck has two webbed feet.* [see *foot*]

fell |fĕl| *v.* Dropped or came down from a higher place: *The snow fell to the ground.* [see *fall*]

fill |fĭl| *v.* To make or become full: *I will fill your glass with milk.* **fills, filled, filling**

find |fīnd| *v.* To look for and get: *You will find your keys on the shelf.* **finds, found, finding**

fine |fīn| *adj.* Very good: *We had a fine time at the parade.* **finer, finest**

fire |fīr| *n.* The flame, heat, and light of something burning: *There was a fire in back of the store.* **fires, fired, firing**

fish |fĭsh| *n.* An animal that lives only in water: *We will try to catch a fish.* **fishes, fished, fishing, fisher**

five |fīv| *adj.* One more than four: *A foot has five toes.* **fives, fifth**

flag |flăg| *n.* A piece of cloth used as a sign for something: *Each country has its own flag.* **flags**

flat |flăt| *adj.* Smooth and even, or without bumps: *That land is very flat.* **flatter, flattest, flatten**

flower |flou′ər| *n.* A plant with pretty petals: *That flower is a rose.* **flowers, flowered, flowering**

fly |flī| v. To move through the air: *Those birds fly south during the winter.* **flies, flew, flying, flown, flier**

fold |fōld| v. To bend one part of something over another part: *I will fold the newspaper to make a paper hat.* **folds, folded, folding, folder**

food |fōod| n. Anything that people, animals, or plants eat or drink to help them live or grow: *Give the dog some food.* **foods**

foot |fŏot| n. The end part of the leg. The foot has five toes and a heel: *I hurt my foot.* **feet**

forget |fər gĕt′| v. Not to remember: *Don't forget your sister's birthday.* **forgets, forgot, forgetting, forgotten, forgetful**

forgot |fər gŏt′| v. Did not remember: *I forgot my books this morning.* [see *forget*]

four |fôr| adj. One more than three: *I have four apples.* **fours, fourth**

found |found| v. Looked for and got: *I found my frog sitting in a box under the bed.* [see *find*]

fox |fŏks| n. A wild animal about the size of a dog. A fox has a pointy nose and ears, and a thick, furry tail: *The fox was running through the woods.* **foxes**

from |frŭm| prep. **1.** Out of: *I pulled my toys from the box.* **2.** Starting at: *They moved from the city to the country.*

fry |frī| v. To cook food in hot oil: *I will fry some eggs.* **fries, fried, frying**

full |fŏol| adj. Able to hold no more: *The basket is full of apples, pears, bananas, and plums.* **fuller, fullest**

---

funny |fŭn′ē| *adj.* Making you laugh: *That was a funny joke.* **funnier, funniest, funnies**

G

game |gām| *n.* A way of playing with rules: *We played a game of tag.* **games**

gas |găs| *n.* A liquid used to make trucks, airplanes and cars move: *We need to get gas for our car.* **gases**

gate |gāt| *n.* Part of a wall or fence that opens like a door: *The wooden gate needs painting.* **gates**

gave |gāv| *v.* Handed over: *My teacher gave me my paper.* [see *give*]

give |gĭv| *v.* To hand over: *He'll give me a pen.* **gives, gave, given, giving, giver**

glad |glăd| *adj.* Happy: *I was glad to see them.* **gladder, gladdest, gladly, gladness**

go |gō| *v.* To move from one place to another: *We will go to the movies with you.* **goes, went, going, gone**

goes |gōz| *v.* Moves from one place to another: *The bus goes to New York every day.* [see *go*]

gone |gôn| *v.* **1.** Moved from one place to another: *They have gone to their aunt's house.* **2.** To have none left: *The apples are gone.* [see *go*]

grab |grăb| *v.* To take hold of quickly: *Don't grab the books out of my hands.* **grabs, grabbed, grabbing**

green |grēn| *adj.* The color of plant leaves: *This green apple is sour.* **greener, greenest**

H

hall |hôl| *n.* A space that joins rooms: *There are many family pictures hanging in the hall.* **halls**

hang |hăng| *v.* To hold or be held from above: *Hang your hat on the rack.* **hangs, hanging, hung, hanger**

hard |härd| *adj.* Very firm: *This chair feels too hard to sit on.* **harder, hardest, hardly**

have |hăv| *v.* To own: *We have new shirts for the team.* **has, had, having**

help |hĕlp| *v.* To give aid: *Please help me open this jar.* **helps, helped, helping, helpful, helpless, helper**

hen |hĕn| *n.* A full-grown female chicken: *A hen lays eggs.* **hens**

here |hîr| *adv.* In this place: *Many ducks live near here.*

hill |hĭl| *n.* A piece of land that is higher than the land around it, but is not as high as a mountain: *This hill is high enough for sledding.* **hills, hilly**

hit |hĭt| *v.* **1.** To bang hard against, or to strike: *The ball might hit the windows.* **2.** To make it to a base in baseball: *The crowd clapped when he hit a homerun.* **hits, hitting, hitter**

hold |hōld| *v.* To take in the hands or arms: *Can you hold the baby for me?* **holds, holding, held, holder**

home |hōm| *n.* A place where people or animals live: *Our home is near the school.* **homes**

hope |hōp| *v.* To wish for: *I hope it won't rain.* **hopes, hoped, hoping, hopeful, hopeless**

horse |hôrs| *n.* A large animal with four legs, hoofs, a mane, and a long tail: *A horse can pull this cart.* **horses**

hot |hŏt| *adj.* Very warm, like the heat of a fire: *The hot pan is on the stove.* **hotter, hottest**

ă pat / ā pay / â care / ä father / ĕ pet / ē be / ĭ pit / ī pie / î fierce / ŏ pot / ō go / ô paw, for / oi oil / oŏ book /
oō boot / ou out / ŭ cut / û fur / *th* the / th thin / hw which / zh vision / ə ago, item, pencil, atom, circus
Key—©1977 by Houghton Mifflin Company. Reprinted by permission from THE AMERICAN HERITAGE SCHOOL DICTIONARY.

house |hous| *n.* A building where people live: *This house is for sale.* **houses**

how |hou| *adv.* By what way: *Tell me how to play the game.*

hug |hŭg| *v.* To put arms around and hold close: *The old friends will hug when they meet.* **hugs, hugged, hugging**

I

I'm |īm| A short word for *I am*: *I'm going swimming today.*

into |ĭn'tōō| *prep.* Inside: *Take these bags into the house.*

J

jet |jĕt| *n.* A very fast airplane that uses hot gases to push it through the air: *The jet flies quickly across the sky.* **jets**

jump |jŭmp| *v.* To leap: *Watch the frog jump into the pond.* **jumps, jumped, jumping**

jumped |jŭmpt| *v. Leaped: The tiger jumped from the tall box to the short box.* [see *jump*]

just |jŭst| *adv.* Barely: *I got to school just in time.*

K

keep |kēp| *v.* To hold on to: *I will keep those cards.* **keeps, kept, keeping, keeper**

kid |kĭd| *v.* To talk in a joking way: *On April Fool's Day we kid with each other. n.* A word used instead of *child: A new kid moved in next door.* **kids, kidded, kidding, kidder**

king |kĭng| *n.* A man who rules a country: *The prince became king.* **kings, kingly, kingdom**

know |nō| *v.* **1.** To remember from having seen or heard before: *I know the story of the Little Red Hen.* **2.** To be sure of: *I know the answer.* **knows, knew, knowing, known**

L

lamp |lămp| *n.* A machine that gives off light: *Turn the lamp off.* **lamps**

last |lăst| *adj.* Coming after all others or at the end: *That is the last crayon in the box.* **lasts, lasted, lasting**

late |lāt| *adv.* After the usual or correct time: *We ate lunch late.* **later, latest, lately**

leave |lēv| *v.* To go away from a place: *We will leave the party early.* **leaves, leaving, left**

left |lĕft| *adj.* The opposite of right: *The 9 is on the left side of the clock. v.* Went away from: *They left my house an hour ago.* [see *leave*]

leg |lĕg| *n.* A part of the body used for standing and moving about: *The knee is in the middle of the leg.* **legs**

letter |lĕt'ər| *n.* A long written note: *I wrote a long letter to my friend.* **letters**

like |līk| *v.* To enjoy: *I like peanut butter.* **likes, liked, liking, likely**

list |lĭst| *n.* A group of names of places, persons, or things written one after the other: *I made a list of foods to buy at the store.* **lists, listed, listing**

live |lĭv| *v.* To make one's home: *I live near my best friend.* **lives, lived, living**

log |lôg| *n.* A thick piece of wood cut from a tree: *Put the log in the fire.* **logs**

long |lông| *adj.* Great in length, or not short: *My legs are long.* **longer, longest**

look |lŏok| *v.* To use the eyes to see: *Look at that rainbow.* **looks, looked, looking**

---

looked |lŏokt| *v.* Used the eyes to see: *We looked at all of the picture books in the library.* [see *look*]

looking |lŏok'ĭng| *v.* Using the eyes to see: *They are looking at pictures.* [see *look*]

lose |lōoz| *v.* To no longer have: *Don't lose your new baseball glove.* **loses, lost, losing, loser**

lost |lôst| *v.* No longer had: *I lost my hat.* *adj.* Not to be found: *Our neighbor's white dog is lost.* [see *lose*]

lot |lŏt| *n.* **1.** A large amount or number: *I have a lot of grapes in my lunch.* **2.** A piece of land: *A large family built a big house on the lot beside our house.* **lots**

low |lō| *adj.* Not high: *That is a low table in front of the couch.* **lower, lowest**

lunch |lŭnch| *n.* The meal between breakfast and supper: *We ate soup and sandwiches for lunch.* **lunches**

M

man |măn| *n.* A boy who has grown up: *That man is my father.* **men**

many |mĕn'ē| *adj.* A lot of: *There are many ducks in the pond.*

map |măp| *n.* A picture that shows where different places are: *We looked at a map of our country.* **maps, mapped, mapping**

mark |märk| *v.* To give a letter or number to show how good a person's work is: *Sometimes teachers mark tests in red ink.* *n.* A spot: *My wet glass made a mark on the table.* **marks, marked, marking, marker**

may |mā| *v.* A word used to find out if something is okay to do: *May I have a banana?*

meat |mēt| *n.* A food that comes from animals: *For dinner we had meat, potatoes, and green beans.* **meats**

meet |mēt| *v.* To come together: *They will meet us at the park.* **meets, met, meeting**

men |měn| *n.* More than one man: *The men sang loudly.* [see *man*]

met |mět| *v.* Came together: *We met them at school.* [see *meet*]

milk |mĭlk| *n.* A white liquid food that comes from cows: *Put some milk on your cereal.* **milks, milked, milking, milky**

miss |mĭs| *v.* **1.** To feel sorry that someone you like is not with you: *We will miss you when you go away.* **2.** Not to reach, hit or touch something: *Hurry you will miss the train!* **misses, missed, missing**

more |môr| *n.* A greater amount: *We will see more of the zoo after lunch.* *adj.* Greater in amount: *Please put more carrots in the salad.* **most, mostly**

most |mōst| *n.* Almost all: *Most of the work is done.* *adj.* Greatest in amount: *I have the most apples.* [see *more*]

much |mŭch| *n.* A large amount: *I know much about insects.*

must |mŭst| *v.* To have to: *I must put this letter in the mailbox.*

■■■■■■■■■ N ■■■■■■■■■

name |nām| *n.* The word by which a person, animal, place, or thing is called: *My name is Jamie.* **names, named, naming**

nap |năp| *n.* A short sleep: *Father took a nap.* *v.* To sleep for a short time: *I like to nap after noon.* **naps, napped, napping**

need |nēd| *v.* To have to have: *I need a hammer to hit the nails.* **needs, needed, needing**

nest |něst| *n.* A home that birds build to hold eggs or baby birds. A nest is shaped like a bowl and made of grass, twigs, string, or other things: *The bird laid its eggs in the nest.* **nests**

never |nĕv'ər| *adv.* Not ever: *I have never been in an airplane.*

new |nōō| *adj.* Never used or not old: *I have a new bicycle.* **newer, newest**

nine |nīn| *adj.* One more than eight: *I have nine pennies.* **nines, ninth**

noon |nōōn| *n.* Twelve o'clock in the daytime; the middle of the day: *We will eat lunch at noon.* **noons**

O

of |ŭv| *prep.* **1.** Filled with: *We fed the elephant a bag of peanuts.* **2.** Made from: *Mother has a hat of the softest wool.*

oh |ō| *interj.* A word said in surprise, happiness, or sadness: *Oh, dear!*

old |ōld| *adj.* Having lived or been around for a long time: *Our dog is old.* **older, oldest**

open |ō'pən| *adj.* Not shut or closed: *The desk drawer is open.* **opens, opened, opening, opener**

or |ôr| *conj.* A word used to join words where there is a choice to be made: *Do you like the green or the blue jacket?*

other |ŭth'ər| *adj.* A different one from the first: *I ate the other hamburger.* *pron.* The different one: *Give me one or the other.* **—The other day—**Not long ago. **others**

P

paper |pā'pər| *n.* A thin sheet made from wood or rags. Paper is used to write and draw on, or to cover walls and gifts: *Please write your name on your paper.* **papers**

park |pärk| *n.* A special area of land in a city or town with trees, grass, benches, and a playground: *The park is near my house.* *v.* To leave a car, bus, or truck in a certain place: *We can't find a place to park the car.* **parks, parked, parking**

part |pärt| *n.* A piece of the whole: *Would you like part of my lunch?* **parts, parted, parting**

pay |pā| *v.* To give money for: *I will pay the man for my shoes.* **pays, paid, paying**

pen |pĕn| *n.* A tool to write with that uses ink: *I like the pen with the red ink.* **pens**

pick |pĭk| *v.* **1.** To choose: *Pick a red crayon.* **2.** To remove by pulling with the fingers: *We like to pick apples.* **picks, picked, picking, picker**

pig |pĭg| *n.* An animal with a fat body, four short legs, a flat nose, and a short curly tail: *The muddy pig ran into the pen.* **pigs, piglet**

pin |pĭn| *n.* A short, thin piece of straight metal with a sharp point on one end: *Take a pin and a needle out of the sewing box.* **pins, pinned, pinning**

plan |plăn| *n.* An idea for doing something that has been thought out ahead of time: *I made a plan for today.* **plans, planned, planning, planner**

play |plā| *v.* To have fun doing something: *We will play football.* **plays, played, playing, player, playful**

plays |plāz| *v.* Has fun doing something: *My sister plays with dolls.* [see *play*]

pull |pŏŏl| *v.* **1.** To hold something and move it toward yourself: *Pull the door open.* **2.** To grab hold of something and take it out quickly: *We will pull weeds out of the ground.* **pulls, pulled, pulling**

R

rabbit |răb′ĭt| *n.* A small furry animal with long ears and a short tail: *The rabbit is eating a carrot.* **rabbits**

rang |răng| v. Made a clear sound like a bell makes: *The school bell just rang.* [see *ring*]

read |rēd| v. To look at and understand written words: *I will read this story now.* **reads, reading, reader**

read |rĕd| v. Looked at and understood written words: *I read ten more pages in my book.* [see *read*]

rest |rĕst| v. To be still or asleep: *Rest here for a while.* **rests, rested, resting**

ride |rīd| n. A short trip on something that moves, like a car, train, airplane, or horse: *We took a ride on that new fast train.* v. To take a short trip in or on anything that moves: *I will ride my bike to the store.* **rides, rode, riding, ridden, rider**

ring |rĭng| n. A circle of metal or other material worn on a finger: *That ring has a red stone in it.* v. To make a clear sound like a bell makes: *Ring the doorbell.* **rings, rang, ringing, rung**

road |rōd| n. A way made for cars, buses, and trucks to go from one place to another: *The road was covered with snow after the storm.* **roads**

roll |rōl| v. To turn over and over in circles: *The pencil might roll off the table.* **rolls, rolled, rolling, roller**

room |rōōm| n. A part of a house that has four walls: *This room is where I sleep.* **rooms**

rose |rōz| n. A flower that grows on a bush and smells nice. Roses are usually red, pink, yellow, or white: *I picked a pretty rose.* **roses**

round |round| adj. Shaped like a circle or ball: *Oranges, plums, and grapes are round fruits.* **rounder, roundest**

S

sad |săd| adj. Unhappy: *Mother feels sad.* **sadder, saddest, sadden, sadly, sadness**

same |sām| *adj.* Alike; not different: *I have the same running shoes as you do.* **sameness**

sandy |săn′dē| *adj.* Covered with tiny grains of rock: *I found many colored shells along the sandy beach.* **sandier, sandiest**

say |sā| *v.* To speak: *I will say a few words to you.* **says, said, saying**

sea |sē| *n.* A large body of salt water. *Sea is another name for ocean. The sea was calm after the storm.* **seas**

seed |sēd| *n.* The part of a plant from which a new plant will grow: *A tomato plant will grow from that seed.* **seeds**

sell |sĕl| *v.* To give something to someone for money: *My parents will sell their car next year.* **sells, sold, selling**

send |sĕnd| *v.* To make someone or something go from one place to another: *I will send you the package tomorrow.* **sends, sending, sent, sender**

sent |sĕnt| *v.* Made someone or something go from one place to another: *I sent a letter to my uncle.* [see *send*]

set |sĕt| *v.* **1.** To put knives, forks, spoons, and dishes, on a table for a meal: *I set the table.* **2.** To put something in a place: *Set the vase on the desk. n.* A matched group of things: *We bought a new set of dishes.* **sets, setting**

shop |shŏp| *v.* To look at and buy things in stores: *We will shop for shoes on Saturday.* **shops, shopped, shopping, shopper**

show |shō| *v.* To point out: *Please show us the exit. n.* A TV or radio program, movie or a play: *I watched a TV show.* **shows, showed, showing**

ă pat / ā pay / â care / ä father / ĕ pet / ē be / ĭ pit / ī pie / î fierce / ŏ pot / ō go / ô paw, for / oi oil / oŏ book / oō boot / ou out / ŭ cut / û fur / *th* the / th thin / hw which / zh vision / ə ago, item, pencil, atom, circus
Key—©1977 by Houghton Mifflin Company. Reprinted by permission from THE AMERICAN HERITAGE SCHOOL DICTIONARY.

shut |shŭt| *v.* To close: *Did you shut the window?* **shuts, shutting, shutter**

sick |sĭk| *adj.* Not feeling well; ill: *My brother is sick today.* **sicker, sickest, sicken, sickness**

side |sīd| *n.* **1.** The surface of an object: *Which side of the box is up?* **2.** The right or left half of the body: *I have a pain on my right side.* **sides**

sing |sĭng| *v.* To make music with the voice: *We will sing at the party.* **sings, sang, singing, sung, singer**

sister |sĭs′tər| *n.* A girl or woman with the same parents as someone else: *That girl with the brown hair is my older sister.* **sisters**

six |sĭks| *adj.* One more than five: *I have six brothers and sisters.* **sixes, sixth**

sky |skī| *n.* The air and space far above the earth: *There are many dark clouds in the sky today.* **skies**

sled |slĕd| *n.* An object used to ride over the snow: *I rode my sled down the icy hill.* **sleds, sledding**

sleep |slēp| *v.* To rest with the eyes closed for many hours: *You will sleep well tonight.* **sleeps, slept, sleeping, sleeper, sleepy**

sleeping |slē′pĭng| *v.* Resting with the eyes closed for many hours: *We are sleeping in the tent.* [see *sleep*]

slow |slō| *adj.* Without much speed: *It was a long and slow ride.* **slows, slowed, slowing, slower, slowest, slowly**

small |smôl| *adj.* Little: *Mice and moles are small animals.* **smaller, smallest, smallness**

soft |sôft| *adj.* Smooth to the touch: *My cat has soft fur.* **softer, softest, softness, softly, soften**

sold |sōld| *v.* Gave something to someone for money: *A man sold yellow balloons at the parade.* [see *sell*]

some |sŭm| *adj.* A few; a little: *I need some help with my homework. pron.* A number or amount not named: *I have some in my room.*

sometimes |sŭm′tīmz′| *adv.* Now and then: *I see them sometimes but not often.*

son |sŭn| *n.* A male child: *My father is the oldest son of my grandparents.* **sons**

song |sông| *n.* A piece of music that someone sings: *We sang only one song in music class today.* **songs**

soon |sōōn| *adv.* In a short time: *We will be leaving for the football game soon.* **sooner, soonest**

spot |spŏt| *n.* **1.** A place: *Move the vase to that spot there.* **2.** A small mark or stain: *There is a spot of jelly on your shirt.* **spots, spotted, spotting**

stamp |stămp| *n.* A small piece of paper with pictures, words, and numbers on the front and glue on the back. A stamp is attached to letters and packages and pays for them to be mailed: *I need a stamp to mail this letter.* **stamps, stamped, stamping**

stand |stănd| *v.* To be up on one's feet: *Stand on your toes.* **stands, standing, stood**

star |stär| *n.* A huge ball of glowing gas far above the earth. A star looks like a small, bright light in the night sky: *The sun is the only star we can see during the day.* **stars**

state |stāt| *n.* One of the 50 parts of the United States: *I live in the state of Texas.* **states**

stick |stĭk| *n.* A thin piece of wood: *Throw the stick to the dog. v.* To stay in place: *Did the stamp stick to the envelope?* **sticks, sticking, stuck, sticky**

ă pat / ā pay / â care / ä father / ĕ pet / ē be / ĭ pit / ī pie / î fierce / ŏ pot / ō go / ô paw, for / oi oil / ŏŏ book /
ōō boot / ou out / ŭ cut / û fur / *th* the / th thin / hw which / zh vision / ə ago, item, pencil, atom, circus
Key—©1977 by Houghton Mifflin Company. Reprinted by permission from THE AMERICAN HERITAGE SCHOOL DICTIONARY.

still |stĭl| *adv.* **1.** Continue to be: *I am still sad.* *adv.* **2.** Without moving: *I can't sit still.* **stillness**

stop |stŏp| *v.* To keep from doing something: *Stop the dog from chewing my shoe.* **stops, stopped, stopping**

store |stôr| *n.* A place where things are bought and sold: *We went to the store for milk.* **stores, stored, storing**

summer |sŭm′ər| *n.* The hot season that comes after spring and before fall: *Summer is the warmest season.* **summers**

supper |sûp′ər| *n.* The evening meal, usually the last meal of the day: *Supper will be ready soon.* **suppers**

▬▬▬▬▬ **T** ▬▬▬▬▬

take |tāk| *v.* To bring or carry to another place: *Take this note to your teacher.* **takes, took, taking, taken, taker**

talk |tôk| *v.* To say words: *I like to talk on the phone.* **talks, talked, talking, talker**

tall |tôl| *adj.* Having a lot of height: *That tall building will be torn down.* **taller, tallest**

tan |tăn| *adj.* A light yellow-brown color: *The color of my hat is tan.* **tans, tanned, tanning, tanner, tannest**

tar |tär| *n.* A black, sticky material used to cover roads and roofs: *The men spread tar on our road.* **tars, tarred, tarring**

tell |tĕl| *v.* To speak words to someone: *Tell me a story.* **tells, telling, told, teller**

ten |tĕn| *adj.* One more than nine: *My birthday is in ten days.* **tens, tenth**

than |*th*ăn| *conj.* A word used to point out how alike or different things are: *I am older than you.*

thin |thĭn| *adj.* Without fat: *My brother is thin.* **thinner, thinnest, thinness, thinly, thins, thinned, thinning**

think |thĭngk| v. To use the mind to make ideas: *I will think hard.* ***thinks, thought, thinking, thinker***

three |thrē| n. One more than two: *We have three pets.* ***threes***

time |tīm| n. **1.** The moment when something happens: *Is it already time to leave?* **2.** The exact hour and minute as measured by a clock or watch: *I look at my watch to see what time it is.* —**On time**—To be there at the correct moment. ***times, timed, timing, timer***

today |tə dā′| n. This day: *Today is my birthday.* adv. On or during this day: *The ducks were swimming in the pond today.*

told |tōld| v. Spoke words to someone: *They told me about the monkeys at the zoo.* [see *tell*]

tonight |tə nīt′| adv. On or during this night: *I will call tonight.*

too |tōō| adv. **1.** More than enough: *I ate too much.* **2.** Also: *I would like some bread too.*

took |tŏok| v. Brought or carried to another place: *Mother took the baby into the bedroom.* [see *take*]

town |toun| n. A place where people live and work. A town is smaller than a city: *There are ten schools in our town.* ***towns***

train |trān| n. A line of railroad cars that travel together on a track: *The train always comes at five o'clock.* ***trains***

tree |trē| n. A tall plant made of wood with leaves and branches: *We have a big tree in our yard.* ***trees***

trip |trĭp| n. The act of going from one place to another: *My cousin took a trip to Africa.* v. To fall or stumble: *Do not trip over the rope.* ***trips, tripped, tripping***

ă pat / ā pay / â care / ä father / ĕ pet / ē be / ĭ pit / ī pie / î fierce / ŏ pot / ō go / ô paw, for / oi oil / ŏŏ book /
ōō boot / ou out / ŭ cut / û fur / *th* the / th thin / hw which / zh vision / ə ago, item, pencil, atom, circus
Key—©1977 by Houghton Mifflin Company. Reprinted by permission from THE AMERICAN HERITAGE SCHOOL DICTIONARY.

try |trī| *v.* To work hard at something: *They will try to get here on time.* ***tries, tried, trying***

twig |twĭg| *n.* A very small branch: *A twig snapped off the branch.* ***twigs***

two |to͞o| *adj.* One more than one: *We own two pets.* ***twos***

U

use |yo͞oz| *v.* To put something into action: *We use soap to wash up.* ***uses, used, using, useful, useless***

V

very |vĕr′ē| *adv.* Much or greatly: *Drums can make very loud sounds.*

W

walk |wôk| *v.* To go by moving the legs: *I will walk to the store.* *n.* The act of walking: *Let's go for a walk after dinner.* ***walks, walked, walking, walker***

wall |wôl| *n.* Something used to separate or surround spaces. A wall can be made of stone, brick, wood, or other things: *There is a large stone wall around my grandfather's horse farm.* ***walls***

want |wŏnt| *v.* To wish for: *Do you want to eat your orange now or later?* ***wants, wanted, wanting***

warm |wôrm| *adj.* Not very hot, but not cool: *I don't need a jacket because it is sunny and warm.* ***warms, warmed, warming, warmth, warmer, warmest***

wash |wŏsh| *v.* To clean with soap and water: *I will wash the dirty clothes tomorrow morning.* ***washes, washed, washing, washer***

water |wô′tər| *n.* A clear liquid with no smell or taste. Oceans, rivers, ponds, and lakes are made of water: *The water is icy and cold in the winter.* *waters, watered, watering, watery*

way |wā| *n.* A path or road that leads from one place to another: *I know the way to the library.* *ways*

week |wēk| *n.* The seven days from Sunday to Saturday: *I was sick during the week.* *weeks, weekly*

well |wĕl| *adv.* In good health: *My sister is not well. n.* A deep hole dug in the ground to get water or oil: *water from the well.* *wells*

were |wûr| *v.* **1.** Took or held a certain place or position: *My cousins were at the birthday party.* **2.** A form of *to be: Her eyes were blue until she was two.* [see *be*]

wet |wĕt| *adj.* Covered with water or other liquid: *The dogs are wet from the rain.* *wetter, wettest, wetness*

what |hwŏt| *pron.* Which thing: *We know what we want.*

where |hwâr| *pron.* In what place: *I don't know where I left my coat.*

white |hwīt| *adj.* The lightest color. *White* is the opposite of *black: Snow is white.* *whiter, whitest*

who |ho͞o| *pron.* What person or persons: *Who is that boy on the stairs?* *whom, whose, whoever, whomever*

why |hwī| *adv.* For what reason: *Why did you leave the jar open?*

win |wĭn| *v.* To do the best in a game, race, or contest: *Our class will win the prize.* *wins, won, winning, winner*

winter |wĭn′tər| *n.* The season of the year after fall and before spring: *Winter is the coldest season.* **winters**

wish |wĭsh| *n.* A strong hope for something: *I made a wish. v.* To want something very much: *I wish I had a pet bird.* **wishes, wished, wishing, wisher**

wood |wŏŏd| *n.* What trees are made of: *Our toy box is made of wood.* **wooden, woods**

word |wûrd| *n.* A sound or group of sounds that have meaning. A word is made up of letters that stand for the sounds: *The word* cat *has three letters.* **words, worded, wording**

work |wûrk| *v.* **1.** To have a job: *They work in the same office.* **2.** To do something that isn't easy: *I work hard to keep my room clean.* **works, worked, working, worker**

write |rīt| *v.* **1.** To form letters, words, or numbers on something with a pencil or pen: *You will need a pencil to write with.* **2.** To make up stories, poems, letters, or books: *I will write about my trip.* **writes, wrote, writing, writer**

Y

year |yîr| *n.* Twelve months, or 365 days: *This is my third year of school.* **years, yearly**

Z

zoo |zŏŏ| *n.* A place where animals are kept for people to look at: *We saw a tiger at the zoo.* **zoos**

Lesson	Test	Date	Progress Chart								
1	Pretest										
1	Post Test										
2	Pretest										
2	Post Test										
3	Pretest										
3	Post Test										
4	Pretest										
4	Post Test										
5	Pretest										
5	Post Test										
7	Pretest										
7	Post Test										
8	Pretest										
8	Post Test										
9	Pretest										
9	Post Test										
10	Pretest										
10	Post Test										
11	Pretest										
11	Post Test										
13	Pretest										
13	Post Test										
14	Pretest										
14	Post Test										
15	Pretest										
15	Post Test										
16	Pretest										
16	Post Test										
17	Pretest										
17	Post Test										